O
V
E
R
V
I
E
W

Mathematics 200
Teacher's Guide

CONTENTS

Author: Carol Bauler, B.A.
Editor: Alan Christopherson, M.S.
Graphic Design: JoAnn Cumming, A.A.

Alpha Omega Publications®

804 N. 2nd Ave. E., Rock Rapids, IA 51246-1759

MATHEMATICS

Curriculum Overview
Grades K-12

■———————————————————————■

Kindergarten

Lessons

1-40	41-80	81-120	121-160
Directions-right, left, high,low,etc.	**Directions**-right,left, high,low,etc.	**Directions**-right,left, high,low,etc.	**Directions**-right,left, high,low,etc.
Comparisons-big, little,alike,different	**Comparisons**-big, little,alike,different	**Comparisons**-big, little,alike,different	**Comparisons**-big, little,alike,different
Matching	**Matching**	**Matching**	**Matching**
Cardinal Numbers-to 9	**Cardinal Numbers**-to 12	**Cardinal Numbers**-to 19	**Cardinal Numbers**-to 100
Colors-red,blue,green, yellow, brown,purple	**Colors**-orange	**Colors**-black,white	**Colors**-pink
Shapes-circle,square, rectangle,triangle	**Shapes**-circle,square, rectangle,triangle	**Shapes**-circle square, rectangle,triangle	**Shapes**-circle,square, rectangle,triangle
Number Order	**Number Order**	**Number Order**	**Number Order**
Before and After	**Before and After**	**Before and After**	**Before and After**
Ordinal Numbers-to 9th	**Ordinal Numbers**-to 9th	**Ordinal Numbers**-to 9th	**Ordinal Numbers**-to 9th
Problem Solving	**Problem Solving**	**Problem Solving**	**Problem Solving**
	Number Words-to nine	**Number Words**-to nine	**Number Words**-to nine
	Addition-to 9	**Addition**-to 10 and multiples of 10	**Addition**-to 10 and multiples of 10
		Subtraction-to 9	**Subtraction**-to 10
		Place Value	**Place Value**
		Time/Calendar	**Time/Calendar**
			Money
			Skip Counting-2's, 5's, 10's
			Greater/ Less than

Mathematics LIFEPAC Overview

	Grade 1	Grade 2	Grade 3
LIFEPAC 1	**NUMBERS TO 99** • Number order, skip-count • Add, subtract to 9 • Story problems • Measurements, shapes	**NUMBERS TO 100** • Numbers and words to 100 • Operation symbols +, −, =, >, < • Add, subtract, story problems • Place value, fact families	**NUMBERS TO 999** • Digits, place value to 999 • Add, subtract, time • LInear measurements, dozen • Operation symbols +, −, =, ≠, >, <
LIFEPAC 2	**NUMBERS TO 99** • Add, subtract to 10 • Number words • Place value, shapes • Patterns, sequencing, estimation	**NUMBERS TO 200** • Numbers and words to 200 • Add, subtract, even and odd • Skip-count 2's, 5's, 10's, shapes • Ordinal numbers, fractions, money	**NUMBERS TO 999** • Fact families, patterns, fractions • Add, subtract - carry, borrow • Skip count 2's, 5's, 10's • Money, shapes, lines, even, odd
LIFEPAC 3	**NUMBERS TO 100** • Number sentences, • Fractions, oral directions • Story problems • Time, symbols =, ≠	**NUMBERS TO 200** • Add w/ carry to 10's place • Subtract, standard measurements • Flat shapes, money, A.M./P.M. • Rounding to 10's place	**NUMBERS TO 999** • Add 3 numbers w/ carry • Coins, weight, volume, A.M./P.M. • Fractions, oral instructions • Skip count 3's, subtract w/ borrow
LIFEPAC 4	**NUMBERS TO 100** • Add to 18, place value • Skip-count, even and odd • Money • Shapes, measurement	**NUMBERS TO 999** • Numbers and words to 999 • Add, subtract, place value • Calendar, making change • Measurements, solid shapes	**NUMBERS TO 9,999** • Place value to 9,999 • Rounding to 10's, estimation • Add and subtract fractions • Roman numerals, 1/4 inch
LIFEPAC 5	**NUMBERS TO 100** • Add 3 numbers - 1 digit • Ordinal numbers, fractions • Time, number line • Estimation, charts	**NUMBERS TO 999** • Data and bar graphs, shapes • Add, subtract to 100's • Skip-count 3's, place value to 100's • Add fractions, temperature	**NUMBERS TO 9,999** • Number sentences, temperature • Rounding to 100's, estimation • Perimeter, square inch • Bar graph, symmetry, even/odd rules
LIFEPAC 6	**NUMBERS TO 100** • Number words to 99 • Add 2 numbers - 2 digit • Symbols >, < • Fractions, shapes	**NUMBERS TO 999** • Measurements, perimeter • Time, money • Subtract w/ borrow from 10's place • Add, subtract fractions	**NUMBERS TO 9,999** • Add, subtract to 9,999 • Multiples, times facts for 2 • Area, equivalent fractions, money • Line graph, segments, angles
LIFEPAC 7	**NUMBERS TO 200** • Number order, place value • Subtract to 12 • Operation signs • Estimation, graphs, time	**NUMBERS TO 999** • Add w/ carry to 100's place • Fractions as words • Number order in books • Rounding and estimation	**NUMBERS TO 9,999** • Times facts for 5, missing numbers • Mixed numbers - add, subtract • Subtract with 0's in minuend • Circle graph, probability
LIFEPAC 8	**NUMBERS TO 200** • Addition, subtract to 18 • Group counting • Fractions, shapes • Time, measurements	**NUMBERS TO 999** • Add, subtract, measurements • Group count, 'think' answers • Convert coins, length, width • Directions-N, S, E, W	**NUMBERS TO 9,999** • Times facts for 3, 10 - multiples of 4 • Convert units of measurement • Decimals, directions, length, width • Picture graph, missing addend
LIFEPAC 9	**NUMBERS TO 200** • Add 3 numbers - 2 digit • Fact families • Sensible answers • Subtract 2 numbers - 2 digit	**NUMBERS TO 999** • Area and square measurement • Add 3 numbers - 20 digit w/ carry • Add coins and convert to cents • Fractions, quarter-inch	**NUMBERS TO 9,999** • Add, subtract whole numbers, fractions, mixed numbers • Standard measurements, metrics • Operation symbols, times facts for 4
LIFEPAC 10	**NUMBERS TO 200** • Add, subtract, place value • Directions - N, S, E, W • Fractions • Patterns	**NUMBERS TO 999** • Rules for even and odd • Round numbers to 100's place • Time - digital, sensible answers • Add 3 numbers - 3 digit	**NUMBERS TO 9,999** • Add, subtract, times facts 2,3,4,5,10 • Rounding to 1,000's, estimation • Probability, equations, parentheses • Perimeter, area

Grade 4	Grade 5	Grade 6	
WHOLE NUMBERS & FRACTIONS • Naming whole numbers • Naming Fractions • Sequencing patterns • Numbers to 1,000	WHOLE NUMBERS & FRACTIONS • Operations & symbols • Fraction language • Grouping, patterns, sequencing • Rounding & estimation	FRACTIONS & DECIMALS • Number to billions' place • Add & subtract fractions • Add & subtract decimals • Read and write Fractions	LIFEPAC 1
WHOLE NUMBERS & FRACTIONS • Operation symbols • Multiplication - 1 digit multiplier • Fractions - addition & subtraction • Numbers to 10,000	WHOLE NUMBERS & FRACTIONS • Multiplication & division • Fractions - +, −, simplify • Plane & solid shapes • Symbol language	FINDING COMMON DENOMINATORS • Prime factors • Fractions with unlike denominators • Exponential notation • Add & subtract mixed numbers	LIFEPAC 2
WHOLE NUMBERS & FRACTIONS • Multiplication with carrying • Rounding & estimation • Sequencing fractions • Numbers to 100,000	WHOLE NUMBERS & FRACTIONS • Short division • Lowest common multiple • Perimeter & area • Properties of addition	MULTIPLYING MIXED NUMBERS • Multiply mixed numbers • Divide decimals • Bar and line graphs • Converting fractions & decimals	LIFEPAC 3
LINES & SHAPES • Plane & solid shapes • Lines & line segments • Addition & subtraction • Multiplication with carrying	WHOLE NUMBERS • Lines - shapes - circles • Symmetric - congruent - similar • Decimal place value • Properties of multiplication	DIVIDING MIXED NUMBERS • Divide mixed numbers • Area and perimeter • Standard measurements	LIFEPAC 4
WHOLE NUMBERS • Division - 1 digit divisor • Families of facts • Standard measurements • Number grouping	WHOLE NUMBERS & FRACTIONS • Multiply & divide by 10, 100, 1,000 • Standard measurements • Rate problems • Whole number & fraction operations	METRIC MEASURE • Metric measures • Plane & solid shapes • Multi-operation problems • Roman Numerals	LIFEPAC 5
WHOLE NUMBERS & FRACTIONS • Division - 1 digit with remainder • Factors & multiples • Fractions - improper & mixed • Equivalent fractions	FRACTIONS & DECIMALS • Multiplication of fractions • Reading decimal numbers • Adding & subtracting decimals • Multiplication - decimals	LCM & GCF • LCM, GCF • Fraction and decimal equivalents • Percent • Variables, functions & formulas	LIFEPAC 6
WHOLE NUMBERS & FRACTIONS • Multiplication - 2 digit multiplier • Simplifying fractions • Averages • Decimals in money problems	WHOLE NUMBERS & FRACTIONS • Division - 2-digit divisor • Metric units • Multiplication - mixed numbers • Multiplication - decimals	INTEGERS, RATIO & PROPORTION • Positive and negative integers • Ratio & proportion • Fractions, decimals & percents • Statistics	LIFEPAC 7
WHOLE NUMBERS & FRACTIONS • Division 1 digit divisor • Fractions - unlike denominators • Metric units • Whole numbers - +, −, x, ÷	WHOLE NUMBERS • Calculators & whole numbers • Calculators & decimals • Estimation • Prime factors	PROBABILITY & GRAPHING • Probability • Graphs • Metric and standard units • Square root	LIFEPAC 8
DECIMALS & FRACTIONS • Reading and writing decimals • Mixed numbers - +, − • Cross multiplication • Estimation	FRACTIONS & DECIMALS • Division - fractions • Division - decimals • Ratios & ordered pairs • Converting fractions to decimals	CALCULATORS & ESTIMATION • Calculators • Estimation • Geometric symbols & shapes • Missing number problems	LIFEPAC 9
PROBLEM SOLVING • Estimation & data gathering • Charts & Graphs • Review numbers to 100,000 • Whole numbers - +, −, x, ÷	PROBLEM SOLVING • Probability & data gathering • Charts & graphs • Review numbers to 100 million • Fractions & decimals - +, −, x, ÷	INTEGERS & OPERATIONS • Mental arithmetic • Fraction operations • Variables & properties • Number lines	LIFEPAC 10

Mathematics LIFEPAC Overview

	Grade 7	Grade 8	Grade 9
LIFEPAC 1	WHOLE NUMBERS • Number concepts • Addition • Subtraction • Applications	WHOLE NUMBERS • The set of whole numbers • Graphs • Operations with whole numbers • Applications with whole numbers	VARIABLES AND NUMBERS • Variables • Distributive Property • Definition of signed numbers • Signed number operations
LIFEPAC 2	MULTIPLICATION AND DIVISION • Basic facts • Procedures • Practice • Applications	NUMBERS AND FACTORS • Numbers and bases • Sets • Factors and multiples • Least common multiples	SOLVING EQUATIONS • Sentences and formulas • Properties • Solving equations • Solving inequalities
LIFEPAC 3	GEOMETRY • Segments, lines, and angles • Triangles • Quadrilaterals • Circles and hexagons	RATIONAL NUMBERS • Proper and improper fractions • Mixed numbers • Decimal fractions • Percent	PROBLEM ANALYSIS AND SOLUTION • Words and symbols • Simple verbal problems • Medium verbal problems • Challenging verbal problems
LIFEPAC 4	RATIONAL NUMBERS • Common fractions • Improper fractions • Mixed numbers • Decimal fractions	FRACTIONS AND ROUNDING • Common fraction addition • Common fraction subtraction • Decimal fractions • Rounding numbers	POLYNOMIALS • Addition of polynomials • Subtraction of polynomials • Multiplication of polynomials • Division of polynomials
LIFEPAC 5	SETS AND NUMBERS • Set concepts and operations • Early number systems • Decimal number system • Factors and multiples	FRACTIONS AND PER CENT • Multiplication of fractions • Division of fractions • Fractions as per cents • Percent exercises	ALGEBRAIC FACTORS • Greatest common factor • Binomial factors • Complete factorization • Word problems
LIFEPAC 6	FRACTIONS • Like denominators • Unlike denominators • Decimal fractions • Equivalents	STATISTICS, GRAPHS, & PROBABILITY • Statistical measures • Types of graphs • Simple probability • And–Or statements	ALGEBRAIC FRACTIONS • Operations with fractions • Solving equations • Solving inequalities • Solving word problems
LIFEPAC 7	FRACTIONS • Common fractions • Decimal fractions • Percent • Word problems	INTEGERS • Basic concepts • Addition and subtraction • Multiplication and division • Expressions and sentences	RADICAL EXPRESSIONS • Rational and irrational numbers • Operations with radicals • Irrational roots • Radical equations
LIFEPAC 8	FORMULAS AND RATIOS • Writing formulas • A function machine • Equations • Ratios and proportions	FORMULAS AND GEOMETRY • Square root • Perimeter, circumference, and area • Rectangular solid • Cylinder, cone, and sphere	GRAPHING • Equations of two variables • Graphing lines • Graphing inequalities • Equations of lines
LIFEPAC 9	DATA, STATISTICS AND GRAPHS • Gathering and organizing data • Central tendency and dispersion • Graphs of statistics • Graphs of points	ALGEBRAIC EQUATIONS • Variables in formulas • Addition and subtraction • Multiplication and division • Problem solving	SYSTEMS • Graphical solution • Algebraic solutions • Determinants • Word problems
LIFEPAC 10	MATHEMATICS IN SPORTS • Whole numbers • Geometry, sets, and systems • Fractions • Formulas, ratios, and statistics	NUMBERS, FRACTIONS, ALGEBRA • Whole numbers and fractions • Fractions and percent • Statistics, graphs, and probability • Integers and algebra	QUADRATIC EQUATIONS AND REVIEW • Solving quadratic equations • Equations and inequalities • Polynomials and factors • Radicals and graphing

Grade 10	Grade 11	Grade 12	
A MATHEMATICAL SYSTEM • Points, lines, and planes • Definition of definitions • Geometric terms • Postulates and theorems	**SETS, STRUCTURE, AND FUNCTION** • Properties and operations of sets • Axioms and applications • Relations and functions • Algebraic expressions	**RELATIONS AND FUNCTIONS** • Relations and functions • Rules of correspondence • Notation of functions • Types of functions	LIFEPAC 1
PROOFS • Logic • Reasoning • Two-column proof • Paragraph proof	**NUMBERS, SENTENCES, & PROBLEMS** • Order and absolute value • Sums and products • Algebraic sentences • Number and motion problems	**SPECIAL FUNCTIONS** • Linear functions • Second-degree functions • Polynomial functions • Other functions	LIFEPAC 2
ANGLES AND PARALLELS • Definitions and measurement • Relationships and theorems • Properties of parallels • Parallels and polygons	**LINEAR EQUATIONS & INEQUALITIES** • Graphs • Equations • Systems of equations • Inequalities	**TRIGONOMETRIC FUNCTIONS** • Definition • Evaluation of functions • Trigonometric tables • Special angles	LIFEPAC 3
CONGRUENCY • Congruent triangles • Corresponding parts • Inequalities • Quadrilaterals	**POLYNOMIALS** • Multiplying polynomials • Factoring • Operations with polynomials • Variations	**CIRCULAR FUNCTIONS & GRAPHS** • Circular functions & special angles • Graphs of sin and cos • Amplitude and period • Phase shifts	LIFEPAC 4
SIMILAR POLYGONS • Ratios and proportions • Definition of similarity • Similar polygons and triangles • Right triangle geometry	**RADICAL EXPRESSIONS** • Multiplying and dividing fractions • Adding and subtracting fractions • Equations with fractions • Applications of fractions	**IDENTITIES AND FUNCTIONS** • Reciprocal relations • Pythagorean relations • Trigonometric identities • Sum and difference formulas	LIFEPAC 5
CIRCLES • Circles and spheres • Tangents, arcs, and chords • Special angles in circles • Special segments in circles	**REAL NUMBERS** • Rational and irrational numbers • Laws of Radicals • Quadratic equations • Quadratic formula	**TRIGONOMETRIC FUNCTIONS** • Trigonometric functions • Law of cosines • Law of sines • Applied problems	LIFEPAC 6
CONSTRUCTION AND LOCUS • Basic constructions • Triangles and circles • Polygons • Locus meaning and use	**QUADRATIC RELATIONS & SYSTEMS** • Distance formulas • Conic sections • Systems of equations • Application of conic sections	**TRIGONOMETRIC FUNCTIONS** • Inverse functions • Graphing polar coordinates • Converting polar coordinates • Graphing polar equations	LIFEPAC 7
AREA AND VOLUME • Area of polygons • Area of circles • Surface area of solids • Volume of solids	**EXPONENTIAL FUNCTIONS** • Exponents • Exponential equations • Logarithmic functions • Matrices	**QUADRATIC EQUATIONS** • Conic sections • Circle and ellipse • Parabola and hyperbola • Transformations	LIFEPAC 8
COORDINATE GEOMETRY • Ordered pairs • Distance • Lines • Coordinate proofs	**COUNTING PRINCIPLES** • Progressions • Permutations • Combinations • Probability	**PROBABILITY** • Random experiments & probability • Permutations • Combinations • Applied problems	LIFEPAC 9
REVIEW • Proof and angles • Polygons and circles • Construction and measurement • Coordinate geometry	**REVIEW** • Integers and open sentences • Graphs and polynomials • Fractions and quadratics • Exponential functions	**CALCULUS** • Mathematical induction • Functions and limits • Slopes of functions • Review of 1200 mathematics	LIFEPAC 10

MANAGEMENT

STRUCTURE OF THE LIFEPAC CURRICULUM

The LIFEPAC curriculum is conveniently structured to provide one teacher handbook containing teacher support material with answer keys and ten student worktexts for each subject at grade levels two through twelve. The worktext format of the LIFEPACs allows the student to read the textual information and complete workbook activities all in the same booklet. The easy to follow LIFEPAC numbering system lists the grade as the first number(s) and the last two digits as the number of the series. For example, the Language Arts LIFEPAC at the 6th grade level, 5th book in the series would be LA 605.

Each LIFEPAC is divided into 3 to 5 sections and begins with an introduction or overview of the booklet as well as a series of specific learning objectives to give a purpose to the study of the LIFEPAC. The introduction and objectives are followed by a vocabulary section which may be found at the beginning of each section at the lower levels, at the beginning of the LIFEPAC in the middle grades, or in the glossary at the high school level. Vocabulary words are used to develop word recognition and should not be confused with the spelling words introduced later in the LIFEPAC. The student should learn all vocabulary words before working the LIFEPAC sections to improve comprehension, retention, and reading skills.

Each activity or written assignment has a number for easy identification, such as 1.1. The first number corresponds to the LIFEPAC section and the number to the right of the decimal is the number of the activity.

Teacher checkpoints, which are essential to maintain quality learning, are found at various locations throughout the LIFEPAC. The teacher should check 1) neatness of work and penmanship, 2) quality of understanding (tested with a short oral quiz), 3) thoroughness of answers (complete sentences and paragraphs, correct spelling, etc.), 4) completion of activities (no blank spaces), and 5) accuracy of answers as compared to the answer key (all answers correct).

The self test questions are also number coded for easy reference. For example, 2.015 means that this is the 15th question in the self test of Section II. The first number corresponds to the LIFEPAC section, the zero indicates that it is a self test question, and the number to the right of the zero the question number.

The LIFEPAC test is packaged at the centerfold of each LIFEPAC. It should be removed and put aside before giving the booklet to the student for study.

Answer and test keys have the same numbering system as the LIFEPACs and appear at the back of this handbook. The student may be given access to the answer keys (not the test keys) under teacher supervision so that he can score his own work.

A thorough study of the Curriculum Overview by the teacher before instruction begins is essential to the success of the student. The teacher should become familiar with expected skill mastery and understand how these grade level skills fit into the overall skill development of the curriculum. The teacher should also preview the objectives that appear at the beginning of each LIFEPAC for additional preparation and planning.

TEST SCORING and GRADING

Answer keys and test keys give examples of correct answers. They convey the idea, but the student may use many ways to express a correct answer. The teacher should check for the essence of the answer, not for the exact wording. Many questions are high level and require thinking and creativity on the part of the student. Each answer should be scored based on whether or not the main idea written by the student matches the model example. "Any Order" or "Either Order" in a key indicates that no particular order is necessary to be correct.

Most self tests and LIFEPAC tests at the lower elementary levels are scored at 1 point per answer; however, the upper levels may have a point system awarding 2 to 5 points for various answers or questions. Further, the total test points will vary; they may not always equal 100 points. They may be 78, 85, 100, 105, etc.

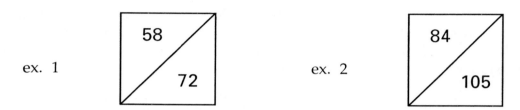

ex. 1

58 / 72

ex. 2

84 / 105

A score box similar to ex.1 above is located at the end of each self test and on the front of the LIFEPAC test. The bottom score, 72, represents the total number of points possible on the test. The upper score, 58, represents the number of points your student will need to receive an 80% or passing grade. If you wish to establish the exact percentage that your student has achieved, find the total points of his correct answers and divide it by the bottom number (in this case 72.) For example, if your student has a point total of 65, divide 65 by 72 for a grade of 90%. Referring to ex. 2, on a test with a total of 105 possible points, the student would have to receive a minimum of 84 correct points for an 80% or passing grade. If your student has received 93 points, simply divide the 93 by 105 for a percentage grade of 89%. Students who receive a score below 80% should review the LIFEPAC and retest using the appropriate Alternate Test found in the Teacher's Guide.

The following is a guideline to assign letter grades for completed LIFEPACs based on a maximum total score of 100 points.

LIFEPAC Test = 60% of the Total Score (or percent grade)
Self Test   = 25% of the Total Score (average percent of self tests)
Reports   = 10% or 10* points per LIFEPAC
Oral Work   = 5% or 5* points per LIFEPAC
*Determined by the teacher's subjective evaluation of the student's daily work.

Example:

LIFEPAC Test Score	=	92%	92 x .60		=	55 points
Self Test Average	=	90%	90 x .25		=	23 points
Reports					=	8 points
Oral Work					=	4 points

TOTAL POINTS		=	90 points

Grade Scale based on point system:

100	–	94	=	A
93	–	86	=	B
85	–	77	=	C
76	–	70	=	D
Below		70	=	F

TEACHER HINTS and STUDYING TECHNIQUES

LIFEPAC Activities are written to check the level of understanding of the preceding text. The student may look back to the text as necessary to complete these activities; however, a student should never attempt to do the activities without reading (studying) the text first. Self tests and LIFEPAC tests are never open book tests.

Language arts activities (skill integration) often appear within other subject curriculum. The purpose is to give the student an opportunity to test his skill mastery outside of the context in which it was presented.

Writing complete answers (paragraphs) to some questions is an integral part of the LIFEPAC Curriculum in all subjects. This builds communication and organization skills, increases understanding and retention of ideas, and helps enforce good penmanship. Complete sentences should be encouraged for this type of activity. Obviously, single words or phrases do not meet the intent of the activity, since multiple lines are given for the response.

Review is essential to student success. Time invested in review where review is suggested will be time saved in correcting errors later. Self tests, unlike the section activities, are closed book. This procedure helps to identify weaknesses before they become too great to overcome. Certain objectives from self tests are cumulative and test previous sections; therefore, good preparation for a self test must include all material studied up to that testing point.

The following procedure checklist has been found to be successful in developing good study habits in the LIFEPAC curriculum.

1. Read the introduction and Table of Contents.
2. Read the objectives.
3. Recite and study the entire vocabulary (glossary) list.
4. Study each section as follows:
    a. Read the introduction and study the section objectives.
    b. Read all the text for the entire section, but answer none of the activities.
    c. Return to the beginning of the section and memorize each vocabulary word and definition.
    d. Reread the section, complete the activities, check the answers with the answer key, correct all errors, and have the teacher check.
    e. Read the self test but do not answer the questions.
    f. Go to the beginning of the first section and reread the text and answers to the activities up to the self test you have not yet done.
    g. Answer the questions to the self test without looking back.
    h. Have the self test checked by the teacher.
    i. Correct the self test and have the teacher check the corrections.
    j. Repeat steps a–i for each section.

5. Use the SQ3R* method to prepare for the LIFEPAC test.
6. Take the LIFEPAC test as a closed book test.
7. LIFEPAC tests are administered and scored under direct teacher supervision. Students who receive scores below 80% should review the LIFEPAC using the SQ3R* study method and take the Alternate Test located in the Teacher Handbook. The final test grade may be the grade on the Alternate Test or an average of the grades from the original LIFEPAC test and the Alternate Test.

      *SQ3R: Scan the whole LIFEPAC.

            Question yourself on the objectives.

            Read the whole LIFEPAC again.

            Recite through an oral examination.

            Review weak areas.

GOAL SETTING and SCHEDULES

Each school must develop its own schedule, because no single set of procedures will fit every situation. The following is an example of a daily schedule that includes the five LIFEPAC subjects as well as time slotted for special activities.

Possible Daily Schedule

8:15	–	8:25	Pledges, prayer, songs, devotions, etc.
8:25	–	9:10	Bible
9:10	–	9:55	Language Arts
9:55	–	10:15	Recess (juice break)
10:15	–	11:00	Mathematics
11:00	–	11:45	Social Studies
11:45	–	12:30	Lunch, recess, quiet time
12:30	–	1:15	Science
1:15	–		Drill, remedial work, enrichment*

*Enrichment: Computer time, physical education, field trips, fun reading, games and puzzles, family business, hobbies, resource persons, guests, crafts, creative work, electives, music appreciation, projects.

Basically, two factors need to be considered when assigning work to a student in the LIFEPAC curriculum.

The first is time. An average of 45 minutes should be devoted to each subject, each day. Remember, this is only an average. Because of extenuating circumstances a student may spend only 15 minutes on a subject one day and the next day spend 90 minutes on the same subject.

The second factor is the number of pages to be worked in each subject. A single LIFEPAC is designed to take 3 to 4 weeks to complete. Allowing about 3-4 days for LIFEPAC introduction, review, and tests, the student has approximately 15 days to complete the LIFEPAC pages. Simply take the number of pages in the LIFEPAC, divide it by 15 and you will have the number of pages that must be completed on a daily basis to keep the student on schedule. For example, a LIFEPAC containing 45 pages will require 3 completed pages per day. Again, this is only an average. While working a 45 page LIFEPAC, the student may complete only 1 page the first day if the text has a lot of activities or reports, but go on to complete 5 pages the next day.

Long range planning requires some organization. Because the traditional school year originates in the early fall of one year and continues to late spring of the following year, a calendar should be devised that covers this period of time. Approximate beginning and completion dates can be noted on the calendar as well as special occasions such as holidays, vacations and birthdays. Since each LIFEPAC takes 3-4 weeks or eighteen days to complete, it should take about 180 school days to finish a set of ten LIFEPACs. Starting at the beginning school date, mark off eighteen school days on the calendar and that will become the targeted completion date for the first LIFEPAC. Continue marking the calendar until you have established dates for the remaining nine LIFEPACs making adjustments for previously noted holidays and vacations. If all five subjects are being used, the ten established target dates should be the same for the LIFEPACs in each subject.

FORMS

The sample weekly lesson plan and student grading sheet forms are included in this section as teacher support materials and may be duplicated at the convenience of the teacher.

The student grading sheet is provided for those who desire to follow the suggested guidelines for assignment of letter grades found on page 3 of this section. The student's self test scores should be posted as percentage grades. When the LIFEPAC is completed the teacher should average the self test grades, multiply the average by .25 and post the points in the box marked self test points. The LIFEPAC percentage grade should be multiplied by .60 and posted. Next, the teacher should award and post points for written reports and oral work. A report may be any type of written work assigned to the student whether it is a LIFEPAC or additional learning activity. Oral work includes the student's ability to respond orally to questions which may or may not be related to LIFEPAC activities or any type of oral report assigned by the teacher. The points may then be totaled and a final grade entered along with the date that the LIFEPAC was completed.

The Student Record Book which was specifically designed for use with the Alpha Omega curriculum provides space to record weekly progress for one student over a nine week period as well as a place to post self test and LIFEPAC scores. The Student Record Books are available through the current Alpha Omega catalog; however, unlike the enclosed forms these books are not for duplication and should be purchased in sets of four to cover a full academic year.

WEEKLY LESSON PLANNER

Week of:

Subject	Subject	Subject	Subject
Monday			

Subject	Subject	Subject	Subject
Tuesday			

Subject	Subject	Subject	Subject
Wednesday			

Subject	Subject	Subject	Subject
Thursday			

Subject	Subject	Subject	Subject
Friday			

WEEKLY LESSON PLANNER

Week of:

	Subject	Subject	Subject	Subject
Monday				
	Subject	Subject	Subject	Subject
Tuesday				
	Subject	Subject	Subject	Subject
Wednesday				
	Subject	Subject	Subject	Subject
Thursday				
	Subject	Subject	Subject	Subject
Friday				

Student Name _____   Year _____

Bible

LP #	Self Test Scores by Sections 1	2	3	4	5	Self Test Points	LIFEPAC Test	Oral Points	Report Points	Final Grade	Date
01											
02											
03											
04											
05											
06											
07											
08											
09											
10											

History & Geography

LP #	Self Test Scores by Sections 1	2	3	4	5	Self Test Points	LIFEPAC Test	Oral Points	Report Points	Final Grade	Date
01											
02											
03											
04											
05											
06											
07											
08											
09											
10											

Language Arts

LP #	Self Test Scores by Sections 1	2	3	4	5	Self Test Points	LIFEPAC Test	Oral Points	Report Points	Final Grade	Date
01											
02											
03											
04											
05											
06											
07											
08											
09											
10											

Student Name _____   Year _____

Mathematics

LP #	Self Test Scores by Sections 1	2	3	4	5	Self Test Points	LIFEPAC Test	Oral Points	Report Points	Final Grade	Date
01											
02											
03											
04											
05											
06											
07											
08											
09											
10											

Science

LP #	Self Test Scores by Sections 1	2	3	4	5	Self Test Points	LIFEPAC Test	Oral Points	Report Points	Final Grade	Date
01											
02											
03											
04											
05											
06											
07											
08											
09											
10											

Spelling/Electives

LP #	Self Test Scores by Sections 1	2	3	4	5	Self Test Points	LIFEPAC Test	Oral Points	Report Points	Final Grade	Date
01											
02											
03											
04											
05											
06											
07											
08											
09											
10											

NOTES

INSTRUCTIONS FOR SECOND GRADE MATHEMATICS

The LIFEPAC curriculum for grades two through twelve is structured so that the daily instructional material is written directly into the LIFEPACs. However, because of the variety of reading abilities at this grade level, the second grade mathematics Teacher's Guide contains additional instructional material to help the teacher prepare and present each lesson effectively. As the year progresses, students should be encouraged to read and follow the instructional material as presented in the LIFEPACs to develop independent study habits. The teacher should introduce the LIFEPAC to the student, set a required completion schedule, complete teacher checks, be available for questions regarding both content and procedures, administer and grade tests, and develop additional learning activities as desired. Teachers working with several students may schedule their time so that students are assigned to a quiet work activity when it is necessary to spend instructional time with one particular student.

This section of the Teacher's Guide includes the following teacher aids: 1) Introduction of Skills 2) Mathematics Terms 3) Teacher Instruction Pages 4) Additional Activities.

The Introduction of Skills is a more detailed overview of skills than that presented in the *Scope and Sequence*. The Mathematics Terms includes a glossary of mathematics terms and a table of measurements. The Teacher Instruction Pages contain guidelines for teaching each lesson. Additional learning activities provide opportunities for problem solving, encourage the student's interest in learning, and may be used as a reward for good study habits.

Mathematics is a subject that requires skill mastery. But skill mastery needs to be applied toward active student involvement. The Teacher Instruction Pages list the required or suggested materials used in the LIFEPAC lessons. These materials include items generally available in the school or home. Pencils, paper, crayons, scissors, paste and/or glue stick are materials used on a regular basis. Construction paper, beads, buttons, and beans can be used for counting, sets, grouping, fractions, and patterning. Measurements require measuring cups, rulers, and empty containers. Boxes and similar items help in the study of solid shapes.

Any workbook assignment that can be supported by a real world experience will enhance the student's ability for problem solving. There is an infinite challenge for the teacher to provide a meaningful environment for the study of mathematics. It is a subject that requires constant assessment of student progress. Do not leave the study of mathematics in the classroom.

INTRODUCTION OF SKILLS

Introduction of Skills is a quick reference guide for the teacher who may be looking for a rule or explanation that applies to a particular skill or to find where or when certain skills are introduced in the LIFEPACs. The first number after the skill identifies the LIFEPAC, and the second number identifies the section. 205/3 refers to Mathematics LIFEPAC 205, Section 3.

Addition

facts to 18	201/1	
1-digit number added to 10's n/c	201/2	*n/c no carrying
2 numbers 2-digits n/c	201/2	
3 numbers 1-digit	201/4	
3 numbers 2-digits n/c	201/4	
1 digit number added to 10's w/c	203/2	* w/c with carrying
2 numbers 2-digits w/c	203/2	
2 numbers 3-digits n/c	204/2	
2 numbers 3-digits w/c 1's or 10's place	204/5, 207/4	
2 numbers 3-digits w/c 1's and 10's place	208/4	
3 numbers 2-digits w/c	209/1	
3 numbers 3-digits n/c	210/1	
checking answers	202/3	
no carry boxes	210/3	

Directions

north, south, east, west	208/4

Even and odd

numbers	202/1
rules to add and subtract	209/5

Expanding numbers

see place value

Families of facts

addition and subtraction	201/4

Fractions

part of an object or set	202/4
addition	205/3
subtraction	206/4
writing in words	207/1

Graphs (Charts)

gathering and posting data	205/1

Measurements

dozen	205/5
linear	
inch	203/2
one-half inch	203/2
one-quarter inch	209/2
(square inches)	209/1

MATHEMATICS TERMS

acute angle   An angle that is less than a right angle or less than 90 degrees.

addend   A number to be added in an addition problem.

angle   The distance between two rays or line segments with a common end point.

associative property   No matter how numbers are grouped in addition and multiplication, the answer is always the same.

area   The measurement of a flat surface. $A = l \times w$ (rectangle) $A = \pi r^2$ (circle)
   $A = \frac{1}{2} b \times h$ (triangle)

average   The total of a group divided by the number in the group.

bar graph   A graph that uses bars to show data.

base   The bottom part of a geometric figure on which the figure rests.
   The number used as a factor in exponential notation.

cancelling   Simplifying a problem in multiplication or division of fractions within the problem.

cardinal numbers   Numbers used for counting. 1, 2, 3, 4.....

Celsius   Metric unit of measurement for temperature. Freezing 0° C., Boiling 100 °C.

chart   An arrangement of data in a logical order.

circle   A continuous closed line always the same distance from a center point.

circle graph   A circular graph that always represents the whole of the data.

circumference   The distance around (perimeter) a circle. $C = 2\pi r$ or $C = \pi d$

common denominator   Fractions must have the same or common denominator to be added or subtracted.

compass   An instrument having two hinged legs used for drawing circles, curved lines, and measuring distances.

composite number   A number that can be divided by 1, by itself, and other numbers.

commutative property   No matter what order numbers are added or multiplied, the answer is always the same.

congruent   Figures that have the same size and shape.

cross multiplication   Multiplying the numerators and denominators of two fractions.

cube   A solid shape with six square faces.

cylinder   A round shape with flat ends.

data   A list of facts from which a conclusion may be drawn.

decimal number   A fraction with an understood denominator of 10, 100, 1,000...

decimal point   A dot separating the whole number from the fractional part of a decimal number.

degree   The unit of measurement for angles.

denominator   The bottom number of a fraction. This number represents the whole.

diameter   The distance across a circle straight through the middle.

difference   The answer to a subtraction problem.

digit   Symbols 0, 1, 2, 3, 4, 5 ,6, 7, 8, 9 which when used alone or in combinations represent a value.

division bar   The line that separates the numerator from the denominator of a fraction.

divisor   The number doing the dividing in a division problem.

dividend   The number being divided in a division problem.

end points   Dots that show the beginning and end of a line segment.

equal to   Has the same value as.   equal = (not equal ≠)

equation   A number sentence that contains an equal sign.

equilateral triangle   A triangle whose sides are all equal in length.

equivalent fractions   Two or more fractions of equal value. To make an equivalent fraction, multiply or divide the numerator and denominator by the same number.

estimate   To find an approximate answer.

even number   Any number divisible by two.

expanded form   Expressing a number by showing the sum of the digits times the place value of each digit.

exponent   The number that tells how many times a base number is used as a factor.

exponential notation   Writing a number with a base and its exponent.

face   The surfaces of a solid figure.

factor(s)   Numbers which when multiplied together form a product or multiple.

Fahrenheit   U.S. standard measurement for temperature. Freezing 32°F. Boiling 212°F.

fraction   A number that represents all or part of a whole.

fraction bar   Also called the division bar.

frequency distribution   The number of times data falls within a particular classification.

gram   Metric unit of the measurement of weight.

graph   A special kind of chart. The most common are bar, line, picture, and circle.

greater than   Has larger value than. 2>1

greatest common factor   The largest factor that can be divided into two numbers.

hexagon   A six-sided polygon.

horizontal   Level to or parallel to the horizon.

improper fraction   A fraction that is greater than or equal to 1. The numerator is larger than or equal to the denominator.

input   Data entered into a calculator (computer).

International Date Line   The 180th meridian. People who cross the line going west, gain a day. People who cross going east, lose a day.

intersecting lines   Lines that cross each other.

invert   To turn around the positions of the numerator and denominator of a fraction.

isosceles triangle   A triangle that has two sides of equal length.

least common multiple   The smallest multiple that two numbers have in common.

less than   Has smaller value than. 1<2

line   A continuous set of dots that has no beginning and no end.

line graph   A graph that shows data by connecting points with lines.

line segment   The part of a line that has a beginning and an end.

liter   Metric unit of liquid or dry measurement.

minuend   The number from which another number is being subtracted in a subtraction problem.

mean   The same as the average.

median   The number located exactly in the middle of a list of numbers.

meter   Metric unit of linear (line) measurement.

Metric Chart of Prefixes

smallest	_milli_	- a unit contains 1,000
	__centi__	- a unit contains 100
	___deci ___	- a unit contains 10
	____unit ____	- unit (meter, liter, gram)
	_____deca _____	contains 10 units
	_____hecto_____	contains 100 units
largest	_____kilo _____	contains 1,000 units

English System of Weights and Measures

Length	Weight	Dry Measure	Liquid Measure
12 inches = 1 foot	16 ounces = 1 pound	2 cups = 1 pint	16 fl ounces = 1 pint
3 feet = 1 yard	2,000 lb = 1 ton	2 pints = 1 quart	2 cups = 1 pint
36 inches = 1 yard		8 quarts = 1 peck	2 pints = 1 quart
5,280 ft = 1 mile		4 pecks = 1 bushel	4 quarts = 1 gallon
320 rods = 1 mile			

Conversion Chart

To convert	To	Multiply by	To convert	To	Multiply by
linear measure					
centimeters	inches	.394	inches	centimeters	2.54
meters	yards	1.0936	yards	meters	.914
kilometers	miles	.62	miles	kilometers	1.609
liquid measure					
liters	quarts	1.057	quarts	liters	.946
dry measure					
liters	quarts	.908	quarts	liters	1.101
weight					
grams	ounces	.0353	ounces	grams	28.35
kilograms	pounds	2.2046	pounds	kilograms	.4536

mode   The number that appears most often in a list of numbers.

mixed number   A number that combines a whole number and a fraction.

multiple   A multiple of a number is a product of that number.

multiplicand   The number being multiplied in a multiplication problem.

multiplier   The number doing the multiplying in a multiplication problem.

negative number   A number with a value less than zero.

norm   A standard for a particular group.

number line A line with even spaces used to represent certain values.

numeral   A figure that stands for or represents a number.

numerator   The top number of a fraction. This number represents the parts being described.

obtuse angle An angle greater than a right angle (90 degrees) but less than a straight line (180 degrees).

octagon   An eight-sided polygon.

odd number Any number that cannot be divided by two.

ordered pairs   Two numbers written in a particular order so that one can be considered the first number and the other the second number.

ordinal numbers   Numbers that show position.   1st, 2nd, 3rd, 4th.....

output   The answer to data entered into a calculator (computer).

oval   A flattened circle - egg shaped.

parallel lines   Lines that are always the same distance apart.

pattern   A set arrangement or design of forms, colors or numbers.

pentagon   A five-sided polygon.

percent   The relationship between a part and a whole. The whole is always 100.

perimeter   The distance around the outside of a closed figure.

perpendicular lines   Lines that form right or 90 degree angles.

pictograph   A graph that uses pictures to represent data.

pi (π)   3.14   Used to solve for the circumference or area of a circle.

place value   The value of a digit determined by its position in a number.

plane shape A flat shape. A plane shape is two-dimensional.

point of intersection   The one and only point that intersecting lines have in common.

polygon   A closed plane figure with three or more sides.

positive number   A number with a value greater than zero.

prediction   To tell something in advance.

prime factorization   Prime factors of a number expressed in exponential notation.

prime meridian   The longitudinal meridian (0 degrees) that passes through Greenwich, England.

prime number   A number divisible by only 1 and itself.

probability   The study of the likelihood of events.

product   The answer to a multiplication problem.

proper fraction   A fraction greater than 0 but less than 1. The numerator is smaller than the denominator.

property of zero   In addition, any number added to zero will have itself as an answer. In multiplication, any number multiplied by zero will have zero as an answer.

proportion   An equation stating that two ratios are equal.

protractor   A semi-circular instrument marked in degrees used to find the measure of an angle.

pyramid   A solid figure with a polygon as a base and triangular faces that meet at a point.

quadrilateral   A four-sided polygon.

quotient   The answer to a division problem.

radius   The distance from the center of a circle to the edge of a circle. The radius is half of the diameter.

random sample   A sample in which every member of a large group has an equal chance of being chosen.

ratio   The relationship of two numbers to each other written 1:2 or $\frac{1}{2}$.

ray   A line with one end point.

reciprocal   The fraction that results from inverting a fraction.

rectangle   A four-sided polygon with four right angles.

rectangular solid   A solid figure with six rectangular faces.

reduced fraction   A fraction equivalent to another fraction that has been written in smaller numbers. This is also called simplifying a fraction or reducing to lowest terms.

remainder   The amount that remains when a division problem has been completed.

right angle   An angle that measures 90 degrees.

right triangle A triangle with one right angle.

Roman numerals   The ancient Roman numeral system.

I = 1   V = 5   X = 10   L = 50   C = 100   D = 500   M = 1,000

scalene triangle   A triangle with no equal sides.

sequence   Numbers arranged in a certain pattern.

similar   Figures that have the same shape but not necessarily the same size.

solid shape   A shape that takes up space. A solid shape is three-dimensional.

sphere   A geometric solid in a round shape.

square   A rectangle with all sides equal.

straight angle   An angle that measures 180 degrees.

subtrahend   The number being taken away or subtracted in a subtraction problem.

symmetry   Shapes with equal halves.

sum   The answer to an addition problem.

triangle   A three-sided polygon.

vertex   The point at which two rays or line segments meet.

vertical   Straight up and down. Perpendicular to the horizon.

volume   The measurement of space that a solid figure occupies. $V = l \times w \times h$

whole numbers   Digits arranged to represent a value equal to or greater than a whole.

Materials Needed for LIFEPAC

Cards (3 inches by 5 inches) printed with number symbols *0* through *9* and number words *zero* through *nineteen*, also *twenty, thirty, forty,* and so on through *one hundred.* Several sets would be useful. (Cereal boxes are an excellent source of cardboard.)

Cards with operation symbols -

plus +   minus −   equal =   not equal ≠   greater than >   less than <

Fact cards for addition and subtraction through *18*

Counters for *ones* and *tens* - these may be cardboard strips (2 inches by 5 inches) - one color for *ones*, another color for *tens*. See LIFEPAC 201 page 10. (Popsicle sticks also work well as counters.)

Objects for counting - beads, beans, buttons, bread wrapper twists

Crayons, construction paper, scissors

Objectives

1. I can read and write numbers to 100.
2. I know addition and subtraction facts to 18.
3. I can learn place value for ones and tens.
4. I can follow oral instruction.
5. I can add and subtract to tens' place.
6. I know operation symbols +, −, =, ≠, >, <.
7. I can write number sentences.
8. I can write fact families.
9. I can solve story problems in addition.
10. I can recognize patterns and tell what comes next.
11. I can recognize flat shapes.

Teacher Notes

Part I: Number Symbols and Words to 100, Addition Facts

1. Page 1 - Have the students write their names. Discuss *Memory Verse* and *Objectives*.
2. Pages 2 and 3 - Have the students practice with cards, reading and putting number symbols and words in number order (1 through 19). Complete pages 2 and 3.
3. Pages 4 and 5 - Introduce addition fact cards through *18*. Set aside facts that the students have not mastered and practice several times a week.
4. Page 6 - Show the students several examples of two-digit numbers (twenty-three, 23) on the board. Have them use combinations of number symbol and word cards to form numbers and words through *100*. Remind them about the hyphen that joins the tens' place and ones' place.
5. Complete page 7.

Part II: Subtraction Facts, Place Value, Listen and Write, Add, Subtract

1. Pages 8 and 9 - Introduce subtraction fact cards through *18*. Set aside facts that the students have not mastered and practice several times a week.

2. Page 10 - Introduce counters for ones and tens. Be sure students understand that the tens' counter is equal to *10* ones' counters. Have students illustrate various numbers *1 - 99* using counters (37 = 3 tens' counters and 7 ones' counters). Use the counters to illustrate ones' place and tens' place. Have the students say the numbers aloud for ex. 2.2 before circling tens' place and ones' place. Dictation develops the students' ability to follow oral instructions. Dictate:

   Listen and write in numbers.
   Listen and write. Circle the number in the tens' place.
   16   26   59   70   98   41   37   62
   Listen and write in words. (Hyphen should be included. Spelling must be correct.)
   Listen and write. Circle the word in the tens' place.

twenty-seven	thirty-five	sixty-one	eighty-nine
forty-four	ninety-six	seventy-two	fifty-three

3. Page 11 - Follow the illustration. Students should circle each set of tens, write how many, and then write the number of ones. They should use their counters to show how many tens and how many ones.

4. Pages 12 and 13 - Use the tens' and ones' counters to illustrate the number *63* (6 tens' counters and 3 ones' counters). Remind students that *nothing* is represented by the number symbol *0*. Have the students add *4* ones' counters to the group of *3* ones' counter. Add *6* tens' counters to *no* tens' counters. Combine the ones' and tens' counters and show they are equal to *67*. Use this method to illustrate addition and subtraction of the ones' place and the tens' place. The students may continue using the counters to illustrate the problems on pages 12 and 13.

5. Complete page 14.
   Listen and write in numbers and words.
   Listen and write. Circle the tens' place.
   numbers   12   39   57   82   words   twenty-three   forty-eight

Part III: Number Order, Operation Symbols, Number Sentences

1. Pages 15 and 16 - Use the number symbol cards and number word cards to introduce these pages to the students. Place a number card(s) in front of them and ask them to find the number card(s) before and after. (32 would result in the students selecting cards showing 31 and 33.) Continue the exercise until the students show proficiency. Be sure to use both number and word cards. Complete pages 15 and 16.

2. Pages 17, 18, 19, and 20 - Introduce the following operation symbols:
   plus +   minus –   equal =   not equal ≠   greater than >   less than <
   Use objects for counting and operation symbol cards to illustrate each one of the operation symbols. For greater than, less than, the students simply need to understand that the open side of the sign is always toward the larger number. Complete pages 17 through 21. Continue to use counters, objects, and cards to help the students understand number order, number value, and number comparison.

3. Complete page 21.

Part IV: Fact Families, Story Problems, Patterns, Add

1. Pages 22 and 23 - Introduce the students to fact families. For ex. 4.4, students should select three numbers and write a fact family. Quiz students orally by giving them a subtraction fact (12 − 7 = 5) and ask for an addition fact in the same family (5 + 7 = 12). Students must have a good grasp of addition and subtraction facts to be successful at addition with carrying and subtraction with borrowing.

2. Page 24 - Follow the 5-step instructions for story problems. Point out the word *together* as the key word in the story, telling the reader that this is a problem in addition. Use objects for counting to represent items in story problems, if helpful to the students. All students should show answers as number facts.

3. Page 25 - Pattern recognition develops students' problem solving skills. Introduce students to patterns by giving them an example. Say the numbers *1, 2, 3, 4* and ask what comes next (5). Ask them to describe the pattern (counting in number order). Suggest patterns of greater than and less than, counting backward and forward, numbers grouped in fact families. Have the students identify the patterns on page 25 and show what comes next.

4. Pages 26 and 27 - Use objects for counting to introduce three-number column addition. Make sets of *3, 1,* and *5*. Explain to the students that *3* and *1* are added together first and then the *5* is added. Do not allow them to count *1-2-3-4, 5-6-7-8-9*. Have them illustrate addition of two-digit numbers by making sets of ones and tens. As the students add the two-digit numbers on page 26, emphasize that they should add the ones' place first and the tens' place second.

5. Complete page 28.

Part V: Number Order, Facts, Operation Symbols, Flat Shapes

1. Pages 29, 30, 31, and 32 - Use the number symbol and number word cards to practice before and after. Show the students a number in number symbols and have them select the corresponding number word cards. Change the order and have them select number symbols for number words. Review the operation symbols. Complete pages 29 through 32.

2. Page 33 - Introduce flat shapes - circle, square, triangle, rectangle. Have the students use construction paper and scissors to cut out shapes in various sizes and colors to reacquaint them with the various shapes. Turn to page 33. Tell the students to locate and color each shape to match the shapes at the top of the page. Have them identify the corresponding colors and shapes on the houses and then draw lines connecting the shapes to the houses.

3. Complete page 34.

Administer LIFEPAC Test

The test may be administered in two sessions. Give no help except with directions.
Evaluate the tests and review areas where the students have done poorly.
Review the pages and activities that stress the concepts tested.
If necessary, administer the Alternate LIFEPAC test.

Materials/Manipulatives Needed for LIFEPAC

    Chart of numbers made by cutting out or copying charts on pages 2 and 3 of
        LIFEPAC 202 and pasting on cardboard

    Cards for number symbols, number words, and operation symbols from LIFEPAC 201

    Fact cards for addition and subtraction through *18*

    Counters for *ones* and *tens* from LIFEPAC 201

    Objects for counting - beads, beans, buttons, bread wrapper twists

    Crayons, paper plate, construction paper, scissors, a brad, paste or glue stick -
        pages 13, 14, and 26

    Pennies, nickels, dimes (play) - pages 27 and 28

Objectives

    1. I can read and write numbers to 200.
    2. I can learn about even and odd numbers.
    3. I can count by 2's, 5's, and 10's.
    4. I can tell time to five minutes.
    5. I can check addition and subtraction problems.
    6. I can tell order by using ordinal numbers.
    7. I can write fractions as parts of objects or sets.
    8. I can learn the value of pennies, nickels, and dimes.
    9. I can add and subtract cents.
  10. I can solve story problems in subtraction.

Teacher Notes

    Part I: Numbers to 200, Addition Facts, Even and Odd, Skip-counting

    1. Page 1 - Have the students write their names. Discuss *Memory Verse* and
        Objectives.

    2. Pages 2 and 3 - Have the students count aloud from *0* to *100*. Compare the
        number sequence on the charts pages 2 and 3 and have the students continue
        counting through *200*. Emphasize to the students that we do no use the word
        and when counting in the hundreds. We say *one hundred one*, not *one hundred*
        and one. Have the students use the ones' counters and tens' counters to illustrate
        the numbers at the bottom of page 2. Page 3 - Tell the students to read the
        words aloud in the matching exercise. Point out the hyphen between the
        numbers in the ones' place and tens' place. Write the *Match* numbers in
        number order.

    3. Pages 4 and 5 - Test the students' mastery of addition facts. Set aside facts (fact
        cards) the students have not mastered and practice several times a week.

    4. Page 6 - Introduce even and odd numbers.

    5. Page 7 - Introduce rules for counting by 2's, 5's, 10's.

    6. Complete page 8.

    Part II: Subtraction Facts, Fact Families, Time to 5 minutes

    1. Pages 9 and 10 - Test the students' mastery of subtraction facts. Set aside facts
        (cards) the students have not mastered and practice several times a week.

    2. Page 11 - Use counters to review *fact families*. Emphasize to the students that

once they have learned one fact (7 + 8 = 15), if they understand the pattern of fact families, they have really learned four facts. (7 + 8 = 15, 8 + 7 = 15, 15 − 8 = 7, 15 − 7 = 8)

3. Pages 12 and 13 - Have the students use the paper plate, construction paper, and brad to make a clock following the directions on page 12. Be sure the hands move freely on the clock. Remember. A hands-on approach reinforces learning for the students. Use the clock to complete pages 12 and 13.

4. Complete page 14.

Part III: Number Order, Place Value, Add, Subtract, Ordinal Numbers

1. Page 15 - Students may use the chart of numbers for number order exercises.
2. Page 16 - Use ones' and tens' counters to illustrate numbers in the first two exercises and in three number column addition, if helpful. Tell the students to add ones' counters and then tens' counters. Compare counters to written problems.
3. Page 17 - Review the correct method of addition using the first problem in each row as an example. Emphasize adding or subtracting ones' place first and then tens' place so students will not be confused when learning carrying and regrouping.
4. Pages 18 and 19 - Review fact families with students. Explain to them that addition and subtraction also work together in larger problems. On page 18, ask the students if *4 + 8* is equal to the same number as *8 + 4* (12). Tell the students that we check our answers in addition to see if they are correct by *adding down* and then *adding up*. Allow the students to complete the page but monitor their work closely to be sure they are *adding up* and not simply rewriting answers. Continue on page 19. Explain to the students that, using the same pattern of fact families, we can check subtraction problems. To check subtraction problems, add the answer to the "take away" number.
5. Pages 20 and 21 - Introduce the words *cardinal* numbers and *ordinal* numbers. Cardinal numbers are used for counting - one, two, three, four…
Ordinal numbers show position or order - first, second, third, fourth…
Use the words *cardinal* and *ordinal* several times as the students work on page 20 so that the words become familiar to them. Complete pages 20 and 21.
6. Complete page 22.

Part IV: Operation Symbols, Number Order, Flat Shapes, Fractions, Money

1. Page 23 - Review operation symbols and number order to *200*.
2. Pages 24, 25, and 26 - Page 24 introduces fractions as part of a whole (point out the oval as a flat shape). Page 25 introduces fractions as part of a set. Page 26 - Have the students use construction paper to draw and cut out the flat shapes and objects shown on page 26. Students may need to transfer this exercise to a larger sheet of paper if their cutouts are too large to be glued on the page. Students need a hands on approach to fractions. Follow the directions. Do not allow the students to simply envision their answers or draw pictures.
3. Page 27 - Use the coins to help students work out the problems. Students may

find several different coin combinations. Any combination of coins that is equal to the amount of money may be considered correct. When the page is completed, review the combinations that would produce the least number of coins. For example, some students may answer *69¢ = 6* dimes and *9* pennies. However, the answer *6* dimes, *1* nickel, and *4* pennies is the least number of coins.

4. Page 28 - Students should be able to read money in number words. Show them that they may add and subtract money using the same steps as whole numbers. When the operation is complete they should label their answer. Review flat shapes.

5. Complete page 29.

Part V: Story Problems, Facts, Time, Even and Odd

1. Pages 30 and 31 - Follow the 5-step instructions for story problems. Point out and have students circle numbers and key words in the stories telling them that this is a problem in addition (see LIFEPAC 201 page 24) or subtraction (older than, more than). Students should show answers as number facts. Some students may benefit by illustrating story problems. Although drawing pictures is not necessary, this method often helps clarify the problem for the student and may also add a little interest to the lesson.

2. Pages 32 and 33 - Students complete fact puzzles, and review work. Read the instructions with the students but allow them to work as independently as possible.

3. Complete page 34.

Administer LIFEPAC Test

The test may be administered in two sessions. Give no help except with directions. Evaluate the tests and review areas where the students have done poorly. Review the pages and activities that stress the concepts tested. If necessary, administer the Alternate LIFEPAC test.

Materials/Manipulatives Needed for LIFEPAC

Chart of numbers made by cutting out or copying charts on pages 2 and 3 of LIFEPAC 202

Fact cards for addition and subtraction through *18*

Counters for ones and tens from LIFEPAC 201- Add counters for hundreds - hundreds counters should be a different color from ones and tens

Objects for counting - beads, beans, buttons, bread wrapper twists

6 inch ruler, pennies, quarters, paper clips, crayons - pages 10 and 25

Pennies, nickels, dimes, dollars (play) - page 16

Ruler, construction paper, tracing paper, scissors, tape, crayons - pages 20 and 21

Clock made in LIFEPAC 202 page 12 - page 24

Objectives

1. I can add and subtract on a number line.
2. I can learn place value for hundreds.
3. I can add with carrying to tens' place.
4. I can learn the meaning of standard measurements.
5. I can measure to the half-inch.
6. I can learn the value of dollars.
7. I can add and subtract dollars and cents.
8. I can draw flat shapes.
9. I can learn the meaning of A.M. and P.M.
10. I can round numbers to the nearest 10.

Teacher Notes

Part I: Number Line, Place Value, Number Words, Ordinal Numbers

1. Page 1 - Have the students write their names. Discuss *Memory Verse* and *Objectives*.
2. Page 2 - Introduce addition and subtraction on the number line. The first two sets for ex. 1.1 should be answered in numbers, the second two sets in number words.
3. Page 3 - Review steps for story problems. Complete match exercise.
4. Pages 4 and 5 - Introduce counters for hundreds. Emphasize to the students that *1* hundreds' counter equals *10* tens' counters and *1* tens' counter equals *10* ones' counters. Use counters to complete place value problems (100 + 30 + 4).
5. Page 6 - Listen and write.

Dictate in words: (*Students write in number symbols.*)

$$\begin{array}{ccccc} 3 & 43 & 15 & 85 & 6 > 4 \\ +\,4 & +\,26 & -\,9 & -\,63 & \\ \hline 7 & 69 & 6 & 22 & 18 \neq 81 \end{array}$$

(*Students write in number words.*)

six   fourteen   forty-nine

one hundred eighty-two

Four plus five equals nine.

(*Students who require it should receive additional practice in this type of exercise.*)

Review ordinal numbers.

6. Complete page 7. Listen and write.

Dictate in words: (*Students write in number symbols.*)

$$\begin{array}{r} 5 \\ +\,4 \\ \hline 9 \end{array} \qquad \begin{array}{r} 14 \\ -\,6 \\ \hline 8 \end{array} \qquad \begin{array}{c} 12 > 11 \\ \\ 15 \neq 51 \end{array}$$

(*Students write in number words.*)

fifty-nine
one hundred twenty-three

Part II: Add, Standard Measurements, Subtract, Patterns

1. Page 8 - Students are introduced to addition with carrying. Begin with an example on the board of *36 + 47 =*. Have the students add *6 + 7 = 13* and ask where they should write the answer. When they see they cannot write a two-digit answer in the ones' place, tell them that they will learn how to carry. Students should look at the first example in the box on page 8 and then complete only those steps in the first row of problems that are shown in the example. They should continue to example two and the second row of problems, and example three and the third row of problems completing just the steps shown in the examples.
2. Page 9 - Follow same procedures as page 8.
3. Pages 10 and 11 - Introduce *standard measurements*.
4. Pages 12, 13, and 14 - Review subtraction, fact families, number words, patterns. Remind students that subtraction is checked by adding the answer to the take-away number.
5. Complete page 15.

Part III: Money, Add, Number Order, Flat Shapes

1. Pages 16 and 17 - Review pennies, nickels, dimes. Introduce the dollar, dollar sign, and decimal point. Have the students use money to illustrate the problems at the bottom of page 16. Answers may vary. Emphasize the importance of writing signs in the answers to money problems.
2. Pages 18 and 19 - Review number order, skip-counting by *2's* and *5's*, operation signs, number words, addition and subtraction. On page 19, point out to the students that there are two-digit answers when adding the tens' place in the last row of problems. *1 + 8 + 5 = 14*   Explain to the students that the *4* is written in the ten's place and *1* in the hundreds place because *14* tens is equal to *1* hundred and *4* tens.
3. Pages 20 and 21 - Review flat shapes. Emphasize that flat shapes are made from closed lines (lines that are connected or continuous). Have the students make flat shapes and the solid shape (square) out of construction paper. The students may trace the pattern or use the actual pattern for the solid shape. Tell them to write the name on the shape, fold at the dotted lines, and tape the shape together. Keep the shape for future use. Compare flat and solid shapes. Always have students use rulers to draw straight lines. They will be developing good work habits.
4. Complete page 22.

Part IV: Facts, A.M.-P.M., Count by 2's, 5's, 10's

1. Page 23 - Test students' mastery of facts.
2. Page 24 - Introduce the meaning of A.M. and P.M. Students may use the clock made in LIFEPAC 202 to illustrate how the hour (little) hand goes around twice for A.M. and P.M. - also, various times on page 24.
3. Page 25 - Have students use a *6*-inch ruler for connecting the dot-to-dot.
4. Page 26 - Complete the first part of page 26. Introduce skip-(group) counting. Explain to the students that we can develop patterns when we count.This allows us to count faster and more accurately. Tell the students to count *40* objects individually (1-2-3-4. . .) Then have them make four sets - each containing ten objects. Tell them to count by tens (10-20-30-40). Discuss how much easier (and more accurate) it is to count when objects have been grouped. Follow the same steps using *30* objects to introduce group counting by 2's and 5's. Make up eight sets - each containing a different number of varying objects. The students should write the name of the objects, decide how to count the sets (circle 2, 5, or 10), estimate how many are in the set, count the set (by 2's, 5's, or 10's), and compare *Estimate* and *Count* by circling greater than (>) or less than (<). (If a set contains 33 objects and the students count by 2's, they will need to count to 32 and add 1 more.)
5. Complete page 27.

Part V: Place Value, Add, Number Words, Fractions, Rounding

1. Page 28 - Use ones', tens', and hundreds' counters to illustrate numbers.
2. Page 29 - Review addition with carrying. Students should begin to understand when carrying is and is not necessary.
3. Page 30 - Review number words. Remind the students that a hyphen joins the tens' place and ones' place numbers.
4. Page 31 - Listen and write.
   Dictate: (Students write in number words using capital letters and periods.)

   Triangle: Six plus seven equals thirteen.
                 Eighteen minus five is not equal to nine.
                 Forty-six is greater than twenty-one.
                 Seventy-two is less than ninety.

   (Students write all following in number and operation symbols.)

   Square: $27 < 51$ Rectangle: Write the number
               $133 > 22$ before and after.
               $53 + 82 \neq 136$ 37,   59,   103,   181
               $47 - 13 = 34$

               (Students must line up correctly and solve.)

   Circle: 23   5   Oval: 86   39
                  12   11   - 46   - 5
             + 51   + 22

5. Page 32 - Review fractions as part of a whole or part of a set.
6. Page 33 - Rounding is an important step in learning estimation. Students who have difficulty using the number line should use objects for counting. For

example, if the number to be rounded is *26*, have them count *26* objects. Tell them to count backward to *20* and count forward to *30* to decide which tens' number is nearest to 26.

7. Complete page 34.

Administer LIFEPAC Test

The test may be administered in two sessions. Give no help except with directions.
Evaluate the tests and review areas where the students have done poorly.
Review the pages and activities that stress the concepts tested.
If necessary, administer the Alternate LIFEPAC test.

Materials/Manipulatives Needed for LIFEPAC

Chart of numbers showing numbers from *0* through *200*
Cards for number symbols, number words, and operation symbols from LIFEPAC 201
Fact cards for addition and subtraction through *18*
Counters for ones, tens, hundreds
Crayons - page 5
Pennies, nickels, dimes, quarters (play) - pages 10 and 30
Current calendar, clock made in LIFEPAC 202 - pages 12, 28, and 29
Tracing paper, cardboard or construction paper, scissors, tape - pages 14 and 15
12 inch ruler, yardstick - pages 20 and 21

Objectives

1. I can read and write numbers to 999.
2. I can learn place value to 999.
3. I can add to hundreds' place and carry to tens' place.
4. I can subtract to hundreds' place.
5. I can learn the value of a quarter.
6. I can construct solid shapes.
7. I can learn standard measurements for inches, feet, and yards.
8. I can read a calendar.

Teacher Notes

Part I: Numbers, Number Words, Place Value to 999

1. Page 1 - Have the students write their names. Discuss *Memory Verse* and *Objectives*.
2. Pages 2 and 3 - Introduce numbers through *999*. Point out the sequence of *one* hundred, *two* hundred, *three* hundred, and so on. Using the chart of numbers, continue to count through *999* substituting *300, 400,* and so on. On page 3, discuss zero as a place holder. Point out that in *201, 0* holds the tens' place when there is no number value in that place.
3. Page 4 - Use the counters for ones, tens, and hundreds to develop the concept of the larger numbers. Complete the page. Play a game with the students using number symbol cards. Put three cards together and ask the students to identify the number. Have the students rearrange the cards to make several other numbers. Talk about the place value of the numbers. Have them read the numbers aloud.
4. Page 5 - Ask the students what Willy Worm sees. When they have completed the dot-to-dot, ask them to tell a story about the picture.
5. Complete page 6.

Part II: Fact Families, Add, Subtract, Money, Time

1. Page 7 - Review fact families. Remind the students that by learning one fact, they have really learned four facts. Several days a week, use the fact cards to review facts the students have not mastered. You may also test students' mastery of the facts by having them recite fact families.

2. Pages 8 and 9 - Review addition and subtraction. Introduce the students to addition and subtraction to the hundreds' place.

3. Page 10 - Introduce the quarter. Discuss penny, nickel, and dime equivalents to the quarter. Use real (play) money to help students find coin groups.

4. Page 11 - Develop the students' understanding of the hour (little) hand. Explain to them that the hour hand moves between two numbers as the minute (big) hand moves completely around the clock. Stress the clockwise movement. Explain that we read the hour using the number that the hour hand is moving *away from*. Have the students use their clocks to illustrate the position of the hour hand at *3:00, 3:15, 3:30, 3:45,* and *4:00.* Students' may write actual or approximate answers to questions for *Write the Time.*

5. Page 12 - Dictation develops the students' ability to follow oral instructions.
   Dictate in words: *(Students write in number symbols.)*
      Write a number in each box. (orange)

$$25 \qquad 36 \qquad 143 \qquad 204 \qquad 315 \qquad 570$$

   (blue)   (green)   (yellow)
   Write the fact family   Add.   2   8   Subtract.   14   12
   for 5, 6, and 11. $\begin{array}{r} 2 \\ +5 \\ \hline 7 \end{array}$ $\begin{array}{r} 8 \\ +9 \\ \hline 17 \end{array}$ $\begin{array}{r} 14 \\ -8 \\ \hline 6 \end{array}$ $\begin{array}{r} 12 \\ -4 \\ \hline 8 \end{array}$

   (Students write in number words.) (purple) five hundred twenty-seven
   Name the next two numbers in the pattern. (brown)
      5, 10, 15...   100, 200, 300...   12, 14, 16...
   Story Problem (red)
      Michael and Larry were playing with six balls. Two balls went over the fence. How many balls do Michael and Larry have now? Write an addition or subtraction fact to show your answer. (Students may illustrate problem.)

6. Complete page 13. Listen and write.
   Dictate in words:
      (Students write in number symbols.) (green)   48   306   250
   (Students write in number words.) (orange)   seven hundred thirty-four

Part III: Solid Shapes, Add, Subtract, Ordinal Numbers

1. Pages 14 and 15 - Have students identify the flat and solid shapes on page 14. Students will have a better retention of solid shapes, if they have the opportunity to create them individually. Have the students use the actual patterns on pages 14 and 15 or trace the patterns on tracing paper and transfer them to cardboard or construction paper. Tell them to write the name on the shape, fold at the dotted lines, and tape the shape together. Keep the shapes in the classroom to help students in learning the names and shapes.

2. Pages 16 and 17 - Review carrying to the tens' place in addition. Review the steps to check addition and subtraction problems.

3. Page 18 - Review the definitions of *cardinal* (counting) numbers and *ordinal* (order) numbers. Write the ordinal numbers on the lines and complete the fact puzzles.

4. Complete page 19.

Part IV: Measurements, Number Order, Story Problems, Fractions

1. Pages 20 and 21 - Compete page 20. (Students may need help with 3/4 inch measurement.) Introduce the standard measurements of feet and yards. Allow students to measure their own feet and compare to the standard measurement for a foot. Discuss the value of standard measurements. (People have different foot sizes.) Students should use actual rulers and yardsticks to answer the questions. Have them memorize the standard measurements for length.

2. Pages 22, 23, 24, and 25 - Review number order, skip-counting, story problems, and fractions. For the story problems, students should write the problems and label the answers. On page 25, the students should show how many parts the whole is divided into as well as showing the fraction. For example, the glass of milk should be divided into four equal parts and then three of the parts circled. This is not necessary for sets. Students may simply circle one of the two hamburgers; however, they should understand that the set consists of two equal parts.

3. Complete page 26.

Part V: Calendars, Clocks, Money, Rounding, Add, Subtract

1. Page 27 - Review addition and subtraction.
2. Pages 28, 29, and 30 - Use the current calendar, the students' clocks, and real or play money to complete these pages. Be sure hour hands are correct on the clocks. The students should practice making change using actual (play) money.
3. Page 31 - Review rounding. Introduce rounding to *100*.
4. Page 32 - *Read aloud.* Have students read number words aloud. Then have them write the order of the numbers in each column. Students having difficulty may need to write the numbers in number symbols before writing the order. Remind students that numbers are arranged in number order working from hundreds' place, to tens' place, to ones' place. Number order is always from the smallest to the largest number.
   Dictate: (Students write in words.)
     sixty-seven one hundred fifty two hundred three eight hundred twenty-nine
   Listen. Circle the number. Read the numbers aloud to the students in any order.
     Complete the number words first and then go on to the numbers.
     Have the students circle the numbers as they are read. Correct while working.
5. Page 33 - Introduce addition to hundreds' place with carrying to tens.
6. Complete page 34. Listen and write.
   Dictate: (Students write in number words.)
     nine hundred eleven   four hundred fifty-nine
   Students may look back to page 28 to answer the calendar questions.
   They will need a current calendar to write today's date.

Administer the LIFEPAC Test
The test may be administered in two sessions. Give no help except with directions.
Evaluate the tests and review areas where the students have done poorly.
Review the pages and activities that stress the concepts tested.
If necessary, administer the Alternate LIFEPAC test.

Materials/Manipulatives Needed for LIFEPAC
>   Chart of numbers showing numbers from *0* through *200*
>   Fact cards for addition and subtraction through *18*
>   Counters for ones, tens, hundreds
>   Objects for counting - beads, beans, buttons, bread wrapper twists
>   Two identical sets of cards (2 inches by 3 inches) - *6* cards per set -numbered *1-5* on the first five cards - on the sixth card draw a smile face (use ten cards numbered *1-9* for more advanced students), crayons - pages 4 and 5
>   Paper or plastic bag, small box of rice (or beans), ruler, roll from paper towels, small box containing a marble, sock, onion, cookie or cracker, tennis or golf ball, watch or clock, bar of soap, towel, piece of cardboard, covered plastic dish containing an ice cube - page 12
>   Fahrenheit thermometer, glass of ice water, cup of hot water (as hot as possible but safe for student to handle), glass of tap water - pages 18 and 19
>   Pennies, nickels, dimes, quarters, dollars (play) - page 22

Objectives
>   1. I can gather data.
>   2. I can learn about bar graphs.
>   3. I can count by 3's.
>   4. I can use my senses to recognize flat and solid shapes.
>   5. I can add fractions.
>   6. I can read the Fahrenheit thermometer.
>   7. I can learn the value of zero as a place holder.
>   8. I can write dollars and cents in number words.
>   9. I know ordinal numbers to twentieth.
>   10. I know that one dozen is equal to twelve.

Teacher Notes
>   **Part I: Number Sentences, Data, Graphs**
>   1. Page 1 - Have the students write their names. Discuss *Memory Verse* and *Objectives*.
>   2. Pages 2 and 3 - Review operation symbols, number words, and number sentences. On the second and third exercises, page 3, tell the students to think the answers to the facts and then write or circle the correct symbol.
>   3. Page 4 - Smile! is an introduction to probability and statistics. The game is similar to concentration. Place the identical sets of cards (well-mixed) face down in three rows, four across. The *object of the game* is to make as many matches as possible before turning up the two smile faces. The player selects two cards and turns them face up. If the cards are a match, they may be set aside. If they are not, they must be put face down in the same place that they were taken from. If the player turns up a smile face, that card is returned to the same place but kept face up. The player continues trying to match all of the face down cards. If both smile cards are turned up, the player calls Smile! The *game is over* when all the cards are matched *or* when the two smile faces are turned up. Play the game six

times. Have the students record on page 4 the number of matches that they made for each game. Discuss the meaning of probability with the students. What was the probability of having a certain number of matches each time they played? Was there a way they could predict their score? How soon did they turn up one of the smile faces? Did it turn up the same time for every game? Why? Why not? Tell the students that their scores are *data*. They will show the data on a graph because a graph makes it easier to compare data.

4. Page 5 - This page illustrates another method to collect data. Have the students identify the data and then show it on the bar graph. Explain to the students that graphs are a valuable tool to display information.

5. Page 6 - Review carrying to tens and hundreds before assigning the page. Students who cannot find answers to the addition and subtraction problems in the balloons will know they have incorrect answers.

6. Complete page 7.

Part II: Patterns, Add, Subtract, Measurements, Number Value, Shapes

1. Page 8 - Students are introduced to skip-counting by *3's*.

2. Page 9 - Review standard measurements for length. Review checking addition and subtraction problems.

3. Pages 10 and 11 - Review fact families and place value. Continue the exercise. Use number symbol cards to make numbers. Have the students tell how the values change as the number symbols move in the number.

4. Page 12 - *Name That Shape* is an exercise to help students recognize and develop their senses of touch, smell, and hearing by object identification. It also develops their awareness of flat and solid shapes. Put the selected objects in the bag and show the bag to the students. Tell them that while their eyes are covered, they should pick an item out of the bag. They may feel it, smell it, and listen to it. The item is put aside (hidden) while they uncover their eyes. They must then answer the questions about the item that are listed in the box(es) on page 12 by putting a check mark by those that apply. Go over the list of questions with the students. The *Name of the Shape* should be selected from the flat and solid shapes listed at the top of the page. (Some objects will be difficult to put in a category, but encourage the students to do the best they can.) *What is it?* may require some spelling help from the teacher. When all items have been selected, give the students the objects in the order in which they took them from the bag. Let them check their own answers to see how well they did. Students may work in teams to complete this page.

5. Page 13 - Have students use 5 objects to make as many sets as possible that total 5. Objects may be used similarly to discover subtraction facts. Complete match and fact puzzle exercises.

6. Complete page 14.

Part III: Place Value, Fractions, Fahrenheit Thermometer

1. Page 15 - Review arranging numbers in number order. Students should select the ones' numbers and arrange those. They should select the tens' numbers and

arrange those. They should select the hundreds' numbers and arrange those. When arranging the hundreds' numbers, they should begin with the largest place value (hundreds). If two numbers have the same value in the hundreds' place, they should compare tens' place. If the tens' place is the same they should compare the ones' place.

2. Page 16 - Work slowly. Compare the drawings to the problems. Be sure that the children understand that they add just the numerators of the fractions - the denominators remain the same. Complete the problems in the boxes.

3. Page 17 - Review carrying before assigning the page.

4. Pages 18 and 19 - Introduce the Fahrenheit thermometer as a standard measurement. Students who are not familiar with temperatures should be encouraged to write some type of answer to the *I think* questions. Remember this is a learning situation. Students should learn the temperatures for boiling (212°F) and freezing (32°F) water.

5. Page 20 - Discuss zero as a place holder.

6. Complete page 21.

Part IV: Add and Subtract Dollars, Place Value, Ordinal Numbers
1. Pages 22 and 23 - Review dollars and cents by writing $2.63 on the board. Have the students say the amounts for ex. 4.1 aloud and then write in number words. Review the value of coins. Any combination of coins that equals the value shown is correct. Explain to the students that problems in addition and subtraction of dollars and cents are completed just as any other problem. Complete the addition and subtraction. Write the dollar sign and decimal point in the answer by bringing them straight down from the problem. Students should solve the story problems and then write a problem based on the illustration. Be sure they show the solution to their problem using dollars and cents correctly.

2. Pages 24, 25, 26, and 27 - Review facts, fractions, place value, number words, ordinal numbers. Students who have not committed subtraction facts to memory will have difficulty when subtraction with borrowing is introduced in LIFEPAC 206. Spend additional drill time on facts as necessary. Page 26 - Students should use rulers to draw lines matching color to color. They should then identify the number and write it at the bottom of the page. For example, red is *300, 90,* and *1* or *391*. Page 27 - explain exceptions - five, fifth, nine, ninth, twelve, twelfth, and twenty, twentieth.

3. Complete page 28.

Part V: Rounding, Add, Subtract, Measurements
1. Page 29 - Review rounding, number order, and operation symbols.
2. Pages 30 and 31 - Practice addition and subtraction.
3. Pages 32 and 33 - Read the rhyme with the students. Review calendar, clocks, dollars and cents, facts and colors. Discuss dozen as a standard measurement. Ask students to name standard measurements for inches, feet, yards. They should know minutes, hours, days of week, months in year. They may write the

current year when writing the date on page 32.
4. Complete page 34.

Administer LIFEPAC Test

The test may be administered in two sessions. Give no help except with directions.
Evaluate the tests and review areas where the students have done poorly.
Review the pages and activities that stress the concepts tested.
If necessary, administer the Alternate LIFEPAC test.

Materials/Manipulatives Needed for LIFEPAC
> Chart of numbers showing numbers from *0* through *200*
> Fact cards for addition and subtraction through *18*
> Counters for ones, tens, hundreds
> Clock made in LIFEPAC 202 - page 12 or any clock suitable for student use - pages 2 and 3
> Scale or scales showing pounds and ounces (size appropriate to weigh the selected objects), two paper bags, various objects for weighing such as blocks, toys, shoes, cans or boxes of food, rock collection, brick - page 6
> Ruler, orange crayon - pages 16 and 17
> Pennies, nickels, dimes, quarters, dollars (play) - page 26

Objectives
> 1. I can tell time to the minute.
> 2. I can learn standard measurements for ounces and pounds.
> 3. I can subtract with borrowing to tens' place.
> 4. I can subtract fractions.
> 5. I can learn about the linear inch.
> 6. I can measure perimeter.
> 7. I can review and practice the things I have learned.

Teacher Notes
> **Part I: Time, Add and Subtract, Measurements**
> 1. Page 1 - Have the students write their names. Discuss *Memory Verse* and *Objectives*.
> 2. Pages 2 and 3 - The first exercise reviews reading time to the hour, half-hour, fifteen minutes, and five minutes. Introduce reading time to the minute Remind students about correct placement of the hour hand. Spend some time with the students giving various times to the minute. Have them find the time on their own clocks.
> 3. Pages 4 and 5 - Practice addition and subtraction. Review carrying.
> 4. Page 6 - Students need a hands-on approach to understand standard measurements. Discuss pounds and ounces. The teacher may work with the students, or two students may work together. The teacher should select two objects and place them in separate paper bags. (Students do not see the objects.)The students pick up the bags, estimate which one is heavier, and circle the 'H' in the first column. They remove the objects from the bags, identify them, and write the names in the second column. They weigh each object (weigh to nearest ounce or pound), record the information, and compare the answer to their estimation of which was heavier. Allow the children to weigh themselves as a comparison to the other objects.
> 5. Complete page 7.

Part II: Number Words, Add, Subtract, Place Value

1. Page 8 - Review number words and place value. Have the students read the number words aloud.

2. Page 9 - Students are introduced to regrouping in subtraction on pages 10 and 11. Review addition with carrying using counters as a bridge to the subtraction.

3. Pages 10 and 11 - Introduce *regrouping* or *borrowing* for subtraction. It is essential that the students use their counters. Begin with a set of *5* tens' counters and *3* ones' counters. Follow each step of the problem shown on page 10, using the counters and pointing to the problem. Illustrate changing *1* tens' counter to *10* ones' counters so that the students understand that there are now enough ones' counters to subtract. Follow the same steps to subtract *36* from *82*. Complete page 11.

4. Page 12 - Review place value, story problems, fact families.

5. Page 13 - Read the rhyme with students. Have them 'fix' the wall by finding all of the blocks that are *1's* numbers and writing the numbers in number order in the first row. They should follow the same procedure writing the *10's* numbers in the second row, and the *100's* numbers in the third row. Students should follow the same approach when arranging any group of numbers in number order. Select the ones' numbers first and arrange them in order. Select the tens' numbers and arrange them in order. Select the hundreds' numbers and arrange them in order.

6. Complete page 14.

Part III: Operation Symbols, Perimeter, Subtract, Rounding

1. Page 15 - Dictation develops the students' ability to follow oral instructions.
   Dictate in words: (*Students write in number symbols, then number words.*)

first bear-	568	five hundred sixty-eight
	309	three hundred nine
	$7.39	seven dollars and thirty-nine cents
	$4.07	four dollars and seven cents

   (*Students write in number symbols.*)

second bear -	427	509	756	93
	$+\ 342$	$+\ 154$	$-\ 325$	$-\ 42$
	769	663	431	51

third bear	$6 + 2 = 3 + 5$	$12 > 5$
	$7 - 4 \neq 6 + 1$	$19 < 24$

   fourth bear - Write six numbers using the number symbols   8,   2, and   7.

2. Pages 16 and 17 - Introduce the *linear inch* and *perimeter*. Using the expression linear inch will help students discriminate between measurement of straight lines for perimeter and square inches used to measure area. Square inches and area measurement will be introduced in a later LIFEPAC. Discuss perimeter of room, etc.

3. Page 18 - Review graphs and operation symbols.

4. Page 19 - Review the steps for subtraction with borrowing (regrouping).

5. Page 20 - Continue subtraction with borrowing. Students may use the number line to find the nearest *10* for rounding. Review counting by *2's*, even and odd numbers.
6. Complete page 21. Listen and write.
   Dictate:

   five hundred nine $18 > 13$ $12 \neq 5$
   $6 + 32 + 101 = 139$ (written vertically)

Part IV: Add, Subtract, Fractions, Money, Shapes
   1. Page 22 - Practice addition and subtraction (no borrowing).
   2. Page 23 - Review counting by *2's*, time to minute, calendar.
   3. Pages 24 and 25 - Practice addition and subtraction of fractions. Tell the students to follow the steps of 1) drawing the line 2) writing the same denominator in the answer as appears in the problem 3) adding (subtracting) the numerators. Use the illustrations to help the students understand why the denominators stay the same. Remind them that fractions can represent part of a whole or part of a set. Use real objects or cutouts from construction paper to make this exercise more meaningful.
   4. Page 26 - Students will need to use actual (play) money to solve some of the problems.
   5. Page 27 - Students should be able to read the names and identify all the shapes listed on page 27. They should also be able to identify flat and solid shapes. Using paper and pencil, administer a spelling quiz using the names of the shapes listed at the bottom of the page.
   6. Complete page 28.

Part V: Measurements, Add, Subtract
   1. Page 29 - Review standard measurements. Complete story problems.
   2. Pages 30 and 31 - On page 30, some students may want to complete the first two exercises without using the number lines. Monitor them closely to be sure their answers are accurate. Page 31, continue to use the counters for subtraction with borrowing. The students should understand that they are not borrowing *1* but they are borrowing *1* set of ten and converting it to *10* ones.
   3. Page 32 - Continue subtraction with borrowing. Have the students count by *3's* aloud. Explain to them that now they know how to count by *1's, 2's, 3's, 5's,* and *10's*. Have them complete the page.
   4. Page 33 - Students may compete with each other to see who can complete the game first by writing the correct missing fact. The students should write the answer to each fact and then move that many positions on the track. The last fact ($2 + 7 = 9$) should bring them to *94*. (You will not want to identify this number to the students before the race begins.) To finish the race, they must figure out that they need to write a missing fact (addition or subtraction) that equals *6*.
   5. Complete page 34.

Administer LIFEPAC Test

The test may be administered in two sessions. Give no help except with directions.
Evaluate the tests and review areas where the students have done poorly.
Review the pages and activities that stress the concepts tested.
If necessary, administer the Alternate LIFEPAC test.

Materials/Manipulatives Needed for LIFEPAC

    Chart of numbers showing numbers from *0* through *200*

    Fact cards for addition and subtraction through *18*

    Counters for ones, tens, hundreds

    Ruler, items to illustrate story problems on pages 3 and 25 (as helpful)

    A book that shows page numbers (about 100 pages) and chapter numbers
      (3 to 6 chapters) - page 10

    Current calendar - page 11

    Pennies, nickels, dimes, quarters (play) - page 24

Objectives

    1. I can read and solve story problems.

    2. I can write fraction problems in words.

    3. I can recognize number order in books.

    4. I can add with carrying to tens' place or hundreds' place.

    5. I can learn rounding that helps estimation.

    6. I can review and practice the things I have learned.

Teacher Notes

Part I: Fractions, Story Problems, Add, Subtract, Patterns

    1. Page 1 - Have the students write their names. Discuss *Memory Verse* and
       Objectives.

    2. Page 2 - Review the meaning of cardinal (counting) and ordinal (order) numbers
       with the students. Show how they are used in fractions.

    3. Page 3 - Students must decide what they should do to answer the questions, how
       to write the problems, and how to find solutions. They will benefit more from
       this page if they discuss and work out the problems with other students (or the
       teacher if other students are not available). Use drawings, a calendar, books,
       pencils, money to help the students find answers.

    4. Pages 4 and 5 - Review addition and subtraction. Continue using counters with
       students who are having difficulty with the concepts.

    5. Page 6 - Discuss patterns with students.

    6. Complete page 7.

Part II: Fractions, Number Order in Books, Calendar, Add, Subtract

    1. Pages 8 and 9 - Review addition and subtraction of fractions. Have students
       practice writing fraction problems in words.

    2. Page 10 - Discuss how number order is used in organizing books. Numbers keep
       things in order. Numbers tell how many. Books are make up of pages. Pages
       are divided into chapters.

    3. Page 11 - Review a current calendar with the students. There are three lines
       under the name of each month. Have the students follow the directions
       carefully. Discuss the pictures and how they relate to the different months.

    4. Pages 12 and 13 - Continue practice of addition and subtraction of whole
       numbers.

    5. Complete page 14.

Part III: Number Order, Place Value, Add, Measurements

1. Pages 15 and 16 - Using the chart of numbers, review number order to 999. Point out to the students that the rules for ending numbers when counting by 2's, 5's, or 10's remain the same, even when the numbers become larger.

2. Page 17 - Review place value to hundreds. Have the students write number words. Students should spell each word correctly and include the hyphen where needed.

3. Page 18 - Use the counters to illustrate addition of hundreds' place. Tell the students to use the counters to make sets illustrating the numbers 385 (3-hundreds, 8-tens, 5-ones) and 241 (2-hundreds, 4-tens, 1-one). Have them put the sets of ones together and point to the ones' place in the example. Tell them to put the tens together. Have them show with their counters that 12 tens are equal to 2 tens and 10 tens. Tell them to convert their 10 tens' counters to 1 hundreds' counter. Show them that they now have 2 tens' counters' and point to the tens' place in the example. Ask how many hundreds' counters they have (6). Point to the carry box and the hundreds' place in the example. Proceed in this manner to complete the exercises on this page.

4. Page 19 - Review standard measurements.

5. Page 20 - Review flat and solid shapes, operations signs, and perimeter.

6. Complete page 21.

Part IV: Subtract, Rounding, Money, Fractions, Add

1. Pages 22 and 23 - Review pages are for reinforcement in subtraction and rounding.

2. Page 24 - Review making change. Students should use actual coins (play) to complete the exercises.

3. Page 25 - Story problems develop skills in addition and subtraction of fractions. Items the same as or similar to those in the stories should be available to help the students visualize each problem. For example, give the students a box (set) of 5 crayons and tell them to divide the set of crayons into 5 parts (one crayon each). Have them describe each part as 1/5 of the set. Ask them to show 2/5 of the set (two crayons). Tell them to read the story and write a problem. When they have added 1/5 + 2/5, ask them if they have the same answer when they put the crayons that represent 1/5 and 2/5 of the box (set) together. Continue in this manner to complete each of the problems on the page. Have the students use real objects to illustrate each story. (A watermelon may be drawn on a piece of construction paper, cut out, and divided into sections.)

4. Page 26 - Practice number patterns. Students use the numbers at the bottom of the page to write six addition facts that equal ten. The only number that may be used twice is 5.

5. Page 27 - Review addition to hundreds' place.

6. Complete page 28.

Part V: Time, Graphs, Number Words
1. Pages 29 and 30 - Review graphs, measuring to the half-inch, zero as a place holder, and number words. Point out that the words at the bottom of page 30 do not follow the normal pattern of simply adding *teen* to the number word.
2. Page 31 - Dictation increases the students' ability to concentrate and follow oral directions. Have the children point to each of the boxes numbered *1* to *14*.
   Dictate in words: (students write in number symbols)

   Boxes 1, 2, 3, 4

28	125	946	42
+ 46	+ 382	− 531	− 26
74	507	415	16

   Boxes 5, 6, 7, 8 $\dfrac{2}{3}$ (6 - *students*) $\dfrac{5}{8}$ $\dfrac{3}{4}$

   write in $\dfrac{1}{8}$ $\dfrac{1}{4}$

   words.) $+$ $-$

   three-fifths $\dfrac{6}{8}$ $\dfrac{2}{4}$

   Box 9   Paula has 6 red crayons, 2 blue crayons, and 3 orange crayons. How may crayons does she have altogether? (*Write the problem and solve.*)

   Boxes 10, 11 (*students write in words*)   forty-seven   three hundred six

   Boxes 12, 13, 14 (*students write the number pattern and the next number*)

   2, 4, 6, ____   20, 30, 40, ____   41, 40, 39, ____

3. Pages 32 and 33 - Review telling time, addition, and subtraction. Stress correct placement of the hour hand.
4. Complete page 34. Listen and write.
   Dictate: (students write in words)

   Boxes 1, 2, 3, 4   forty-six   three hundred seventy   four-fifths   thirteen

Administer LIFEPAC Test
   The test may be administered in two sessions. Give no help except with directions.
   Evaluate the tests and review areas where the students have done poorly.
   Review the pages and activities that stress the concepts tested.
   If necessary, administer the Alternate LIFEPAC test.

Materials/Manipulatives Needed for LIFEPAC
    Chart of numbers showing numbers from *0* through *200*
    Fact cards for addition and subtraction through *18*
    Counters for ones, tens, hundreds
    Crayons
    120 objects for counting (beans, buttons, bread twists, toothpicks) - page 3
    Pennies, nickels, dimes, quarters, dollars (play) - pages 10 and 11
    Ruler - page 16
    Atlas or road map - page 26
    Cup, pint, quart, and gallon containers, beans, rice, or water - page 30

Objectives
1. I can learn group counting.
2. I can learn mental addition and subtraction.
3. I can change coins to coins of equal value.
4. I can learn about length and width.
5. I can name the fraction part of a set.
6. I can add with carrying to
    tens' place and hundreds' place.
7. I can learn directions for north, south, east, west.
8. I can learn standard measurements
    for cups, pints, quarts, and gallons.
9. I can review and practice
    the things I have learned.

Teacher Notes
  Part I: Number Order, Skip-(group) Counting, Add, Subtract, Even, Odd
1. Page 1 - Have the students write their names. Discuss *Memory Verse* and *Objectives*.
2. Pages 2 and 3 - Review number order. Clouds should be colored the same color as the lines. Page 3 teaches that counting by *2's, 5's,* and *10's* can be faster and more accurate. Continue the practice with other large numbers.
3. Pages 4 and 5 - Review steps for subtraction with borrowing.
4. Page 6 - Have the students solve the first few 'think' problems by saying the steps aloud. If they are successful allow them to complete the *thinking* problems independently. Review the meaning of *family of facts*.
5. Complete page 7.

  Part II: Operation Symbols, Money, Add, Subtract
1. Page 8 - Explain to the students that a number sentence may be written in number symbols or number words. Review the number symbols and the operation symbols. Be sure the students recognize these two categories. When the students have completed the page, ask them to say each sentence aloud in words.
    For example: *Six plus seven is equal to thirteen.*   *Seven plus three is equal to ten.*
                       Two plus three is less than eight.   *Seven plus four is equal to eleven.*

2. Page 9 - Review ones', tens', and hundreds' places. Have the students count by *3's* to *30*.
3. Pages 10 and 11- This exercise teaches students that a certain amount of money may be represented by several different combinations of coins. Guide the students into finding the least number of coins possible for a given amount of money. Students should use actual or play coins to understand the exercise. On page 11, have the students illustrate the value of each object using dollars and coins. Allow the students to develop several possibilities and then decide on the the least number of coins (and dollars) possible. This process develops mental arithmetic. For example: *$1.36* - How many quarters in *36¢*? (1) How much is left? (11¢) How many dimes in *11¢*? (1) How much is left? (1¢) *1¢ = 1* penny.   The addition problems should be written using the dollars and cents, not the coins. Review with the students that the decimal points must be lined up directly under each other in a manner similar to lining the ones', tens', and hundreds' places. Students should label their answers with decimal points and dollar signs. Remind them that we do not use the dollar sign and cent sign together.
4. Pages 12 and 13 - Review addition and subtraction problems for tens and hundreds written horizontally and vertically. Encourage students to be careful and accurate in writing numbers and lining up columns.
5. Complete page 14.

Part III: Ordinal Numbers, Length, Width, Perimeter, Fractions
1. Pages 15 and 16 - Review ordinal numbers, length, width, and perimeter.
2. Page 17 - Have the students read the rhyme and answer the questions. Students may give an answer without writing a problem; however, each student should be quizzed as to how he/she arrived at the answer.
3. Pages 18 and 19 - Tell the students to look at the objects in the two columns. Ask them which column illustrates fractions that are part of a whole and which column illustrates fractions as part of a set. Have them complete page 18. Review the steps for addition and subtraction of fractions on page 19.
4. Page 20 - Listen and write.
    Dictate:
    First Orange - Students write the numbers 0 through 11.
    Second Orange - Students write six facts equaling 11.
    Use each number (0-11) once.
    Third Orange - Students solve mentally - write just the answer.
    $6 - 3 + 4 =$ $2 + 1 - 3 =$ $8 + 5 - 7 + 2 =$ $6 - 3 + 5 + 4 =$
    Fourth Orange - Count by 2's beginning with 6.
    Count by 5's beginning with 15.
    Count by 10's beginning with 30.
    Fifth Orange - Read the story problem.
    Students write the problem and solve for the answer.
    1. Tom has 60¢. He wants to buy a book that costs 85¢. How much more money does Tom need to buy the book?
    2. There are 34 children in the group. 18 are girls.

64

>>> How many boys are there in the group?
>>> 3. Laura has 2 quarters, 3 dimes, 1 nickel, and 2 pennies.
>>> How much money does Laura have?

> 5. Complete page 21. Listen and write.
>   *Dictate:*
>   *apple:* solve mentally $2 + 5 - 3 + 6 =$ *banana:* count by 2's, start with 6
>   *orange 1:* $2/8 + 1/8 =$ *orange 2:* $5/9 - 2/9 =$
>   *orange 3:* How much money? 2 quarters, 3 dimes, 2 pennies
>   *orange 4:* Jim has a package of 12 stamps. He needs 28 stamps.
>   How many more stamps does he need to buy?

Part IV: Number Words, Rounding, Add, Subtract, Directions - N, S, E, W

1. Pages 22, 23, 24, and 25 - Review number words, rounding, addition, and subtraction. Introduce carrying to both ones' and tens' place in three-digit numbers. Students who have difficulty with the concept should use counters.

2. Pages 26 and 27 - Begin the discussion of directions by identifying directions of north, south, east, and west in the classroom. Use an atlas or road map to give the students a general idea of directions on a map. Ask them to point to and identify the direction they would go from the classroom to a store, a playground, a friend's house. Pages 26 and 27 should be completed in a group or with the teacher.

3. Complete page 28.

Part V: Place Value, Measurements, Check Addition and Subtraction

1. Page 29 - Review place value, addition, and subtraction. Remind students that in arranging digits such as 3, 0, 5 for smallest number, we do not need to write 0 in the hundreds' place. 0 3 5

2. Pages 30 and 31 - Introduce the standard measurements of cups, pints, quarts, and gallons. Allow students to participate using actual measuring tools. Students should memorize standard measurements for volume.

3. Pages 32 and 33 - Addition problems may be checked by adding down and adding up. Subtraction problems are checked by adding the take-away number to the answer.

4. Complete page 34.

Administer LIFEPAC Test

The test may be administered in two sessions. Give no help except with directions.
Evaluate the tests and review areas where the students have done poorly.
Review the pages and activities that stress the concepts tested.
If necessary, administer the Alternate LIFEPAC test.

Materials/Manipulatives Needed for LIFEPAC

    Chart of numbers showing numbers from *0* through *200*

    Fact cards for addition and subtraction through *18*

    Counters for ones, tens, hundreds

    Ruler, crayons - pages 2, 3, and 12

    Cardboard and brad to make a spinner, crayons - pages 8 and 9

    Items and measuring tools to illustrate exercises - pages 15 and 16

    Ruler, scissors, construction paper, crayons - page 17

    Pennies, nickels, dimes, quarters, dollars - page 19

Objectives

1. I can learn about area and square measurement.
2. I can add three numbers with
   carrying to tens' place.
3. I can collect data and post it to a bar graph.
4. I can measure to the quarter-inch.
5. I can learn directions for north, south, east, west.
6. I can learn to change coins to cents.
7. I can review and practice
   the things I have learned.

Teacher Notes

Part I: Perimeter, Area, Place Value, Add

1. Page 1 - Have the students write their names. Discuss *Memory Verse* and *Objectives*.
2. Pages 2 and 3 - Review measurements, perimeter, length and width. Discuss the word *surface* and introduce *area* as a measurement. Have the students complete the exercises on page 3. As a reinforcement exercise, have the students use pencil, ruler, and plain paper to draw several more rectangles. Instruct them to use a crayon to draw around the perimeter of each rectangle. Then, have them draw in the square inches, cut the rectangles up into the square inch blocks, and put the rectangles back together. Emphasize *square inch*.
3. Page 4 - Review place value.
4. Page 5 - Introduce carrying in addition when adding three numbers. Students having difficulty should use counters for ones and tens.
5. Page 6 - Review addition. Rewrite horizontal problems.
6. Complete page 7.

Part II: Data, Graphs, Quarter-inch, Directions - N, S, E, W

1. Pages 8 and 9 - Students will need to use cardboard and a brad to make the spinner. The spinner should be as balanced as possible so the pointer has an equal possibility of stopping at any number. Tell the students to spin the pointer twenty times and to record where it stops each time. They should organize the data by answering the questions at the top of page 9. Review probability. Did the pointer stop at one number more often than another? What was the probability that it would? Explain to the students that a graph

is a visual method used to show the results of the data. They should illustrate the data from the top of the page on the graph.
2. Page 10 - Review subtraction.
3. Page 11- Listen and write.
   Dictate:
   First Heart - Students begin at 150 and count backward by 1's to 140.
   Second Heart - Students begin a 720 and count forward by 2's to 730.
   Third Heart - Dictate problems in words. Students should do mental arithmetic and write just answers.

9 + 3 =	16 + 2 =	2 + 5 + 8 =	7 + 3 + 6 =
12 − 6 =	8 − 3 + 2 =	13 − 5 + 4 =	6 + 7 − 2 =

   Fourth Heart - Students write the number before and the number after.

759	207	381	900

   Fifth Heart - Dictate problems in words. Students write problems and solve.

46	58	75	82
+ 27	+ 29	− 38	− 17

4. Pages 12 and 13 - Introduce students to measuring to the quarter-inch on a ruler. Always have students use a ruler to draw lines. Do not allow them to free hand. Have students identify directions for north, south, east, and west in the classroom and on page 13. After the students have written the direction that Jack is going (N, S, E, or W), have them use their rulers to measure some of the lines. Allow them to complete the page by drawing a picture of Jack in a snowpile.
5. Complete page 14.   Listen and write.
   Dictate:
   Write the number before 146, the number after 159.
   Write just the answer. 7 + 2 + 6 =, 4 + 4 + 6 =, 7 − 5 + 8 =, 12 − 4 − 6 =
   Students write the problem and solve.
   49 + 46 =, 75 + 38 =, 92 − 57 =, 61 − 43 =

Part III: Measurements, Perimeter, Area, Fractions, Money
1. Pages 15 and 16 - Review measurements and time. Have actual items and measuring tools available for students to work out the answers to the questions. On page 16, students should tell as closely as possible when they have done or expect to do these activities.
2. Page 17 - Complete exercises in perimeter and area. The four rectangles listed at the bottom of the page should be drawn to actual size by the students on the construction paper. Have them use their rulers to measure the perimeter. Have them use the square inch that they cut out to find the area. Be sure that they are labeling their answers correctly in linear or square inches.
3. Page 18 - Review ordinal numbers. Use story problems to round to the nearest *10*.
4. Page 19 - Change coins to cents. Add the cents. Practice mental addition and subtraction. Students having difficulty may use the chart of numbers or write the problems vertically.

5. Page 20 - Students solve story problems.
6. Complete page 21.

Part IV: Number Words, Add, Subtract, Fractions, Operation Symbols
1. Pages 22, 23, and 24 - Review number words and symbols, addition and subtraction, number order, and fact families. Use counters where helpful.
2. Page 25 - Review addition and subtraction of fractions. Remind the students to follow the steps: 1) draw a line 2) write the bottom number 3) add or subtract the top number.
3. Pages 26 and 27 - Review operation symbols, fractions as words, addition and subtraction of money, checking addition and subtraction problems. Remind the students, in *greater than* and *less than*, the open side of the symbol is always toward the larger number.
4. Complete page 28.

Part V: Add, Subtract, Even, Odd, Shapes
1. Page 29 - Listen and write.
   Dictate:

First Triangle -	Students draw hands on clocks. 7:15 8:30 2:45 5:18
Second Triangle -	Students write the cents. They may use actual (play) money.

   2 quarters, 1 dime, 2 pennies   3 dimes, 3 nickels, 1 penny
   1 quarter, 3 dimes, 2 nickels   4 dimes, 5 nickels, 3 pennies

Third Triangle -	Students write addition facts for 7 starting with 7 + 0. (Do not dictate facts - students should know them.)
Fourth Triangle -	Students solve mental arithmetic problems.

   $6 - 2 + 5 =$ $7 + 4 + 6 =$ $9 + 8 - 4 =$
   $36 + 3 - 1 =$ $17 + 2 - 5 =$ $46 + 3 - 7 =$

Fifth Triangle -	Students write in number words.

   seven hundred thirteen   six hundred thirty-two

Sixth Triangle -	Dictate in words. Students write in number and operation symbols.

   $36 < 42$ $64 > 29$ $16 + 2 = 18$ $24 - 5 \neq 20$
2. Pages 30 and 31 - Review addition and subtraction. Rewrite horizontal problems.
3. Page 32 - Have the students identify each number in the problem as well as the answer as *even* or *odd*. Ask them to find a pattern that will let them estimate if they have a correct answer when adding numbers.
   even + even or *odd + odd = even*   *odd + even* or *even + odd = odd*
4. Page 33 - Read the rhyme with the students and have them draw dot-to-dot counting by 5's. They may color the pinwheel.
5. Complete page 34. - Listen and write.
   Dictate: Draw the hands on the clock for 5:47.

Write the cents.	1 quarter, 2 dimes, 4 pennies	
Mental arithmetic	$6 + 2 + 7 =$	$3 - 1 + 8 =$
Words and symbols	(word) eleven	(symbols) $27 < 45$

Administer LIFEPAC Test

The test may be administered in two sessions. Give no help except with directions.

Evaluate the tests and review areas where the students have done poorly.

Review the pages and activities that stress the concepts tested.

If necessary, administer the Alternate LIFEPAC test.

Materials/Manipulatives Needed for LIFEPAC
　　Chart of numbers showing numbers from *0* through *200*
　　Fact cards for addition and subtraction through *18*
　　Counters for ones, tens, hundreds
　　Objects for counting
　　Pennies, nickels, dimes, quarters, dollars (play) - page 9
　　Ruler - page 17
　　Digital clock - page 16

Objectives
　　1.　　I can add without the carry box.
　　2.　　I can round numbers to hundreds' place.
　　3.　　I can learn rules for adding even and
　　　　　odd numbers.
　　4.　　I can read a digital clock.
　　5.　　I can learn to give sensible answers
　　　　　to story problems.
　　6.　　I can find solid shapes in objects.
　　7.　　I can review and practice
　　　　　the things I have learned.

Teacher Notes
　　Part I: Add, Rounding, Story Problems
　　　1. Page 1 - Have the students write their names. Discuss *Memory Verse* and *Objectives*.
　　　2. Page 2 - Introduce addition of three numbers in the hundreds - no carry.
　　　3. Page 3 - Students should identify problems in which they do and do not need to carry. They should learn to complete addition with carrying without the use of the carry box.
　　　4. Pages 4 and 5 - Students review rounding to the nearest 10 and are introduced to rounding to the nearest 100. The chart of numbers, counters, and the number line are helpful in explaining this concept to the students.
　　　5. Page 6 - Students complete the story problems.
　　　6. Complete page 7.

　　Part II: Subtract, Even and Odd, Money, Place Value, Ordinal Numbers
　　　1. Page 8 - Review subtraction. Students should continue to use the boxes for purposes of borrowing or regrouping. They should rewrite the horizontal problems (not facts) as vertical problems.
　　　2. Pages 9, 10 and 11 - The even or odd rule is a useful tool for students to decide whether or not they have a reasonable answer to a problem. Use actual (play) money to assist students in solving money problems. Review the decimal point and dollar sign. Point out that the cent sign is used only when writing cents alone; however, cents also may be written using the dollar sign and decimal point. Explain the use of the zero as a place holder in writing money just as it is used in other numbers. Write several examples of money on the board, both in

numbers and in words, to develop the lesson. Students should not be distracted by the decimal point and dollar sign in solving addition and subtraction problems. They should complete the problems as they have learned, carrying or borrowing as necessary, and then placing the signs in the final answer.

3. Pages 12 and 13 - Review place value, number words and symbols, ordinal numbers. Read the rhyme on page 13 with the students and have them fill in the blanks. Tell them to write or tell a story about the *missing word*.

4. Complete page 14.

Part III: Graphs, Digital Clocks, Perimeter, Area, Add, Subtract

1. Page 15 - Review a current calendar and the thermometer with the students. Have them read the current temperature - inside and outside. Tell the students to read the directions on page 15 and complete the bar graph. Have them keep a similar record for the current month and make a corresponding graph.

2. Page 16 - Review telling time on a dial clock. Introduce the digital clock. Have one available for demonstration.

3. Page 17 - Review the meaning of linear and square measurement, length, width, perimeter and area. Additional activities may include measurements of real objects or rooms using ruler and yardstick.

4. Pages 18, 19, and 20 - Review addition, subtraction, fact families, and number order.

5. Complete page 21.

Part IV: Fractions, Add, Subtract, Sensible Answers

1. Pages 22 and 23 - Use objects for counting to help students identify fractions as part of a set. Have them use a single item (toothpick, straw, piece of paper, paper roll) and cut into parts to illustrate fractions as part of a whole. Students should follow the correct steps for addition and subtraction of fractions: 1) draw the line 2) write the bottom number of the fraction 3) add or subtract the top numbers.

2. Pages 24 and 25 - Review checking addition problems by adding down and adding up and checking subtraction problems by adding the answer to the take-away number. Monitor the students' work carefully to be sure they are actually checking problems and not simply rewriting answers.

3. Pages 26 and 27 - Students should complete pages 26 and 27 as independently as possible. Encourage them to look for sensible answers.

4. Complete page 28.

Part V: Patterns, Number Order, Number Words, Solid Shapes, Story Problems

1. Page 29 - Allow students to complete the page and then review each problem. Be sure the students understand the pattern to each problem before continuing.

2. Page 30 - Review number order.

3. Page 31 - Review flat and solid shapes with the students. Have them recite the names of the flat shapes (rectangle, square, triangle, circle, oval). Have them match the name of the solid shape to its shape by writing the number (1, 2, 3, 4,

or 5). Tell the students to look at each picture, identify the solid shape that it most closely resembles, and write the number of the shape on the line.

4. Page 32 - Complete problems in number words.
5. Pages 33 and 34 - Students may write a story problem illustrating each of the pictures, or they may write a problem in numbers and explain the story orally. Complete page 34.

Administer LIFEPAC Test

The test may be administered in two sessions. Give no help except with directions.
Evaluate the tests and review areas where the students have done poorly.
Review the pages and activities that stress the concepts tested.
If necessary, administer the Alternate LIFEPAC test.

ADDITIONAL ACTIVITIES

1. Plan **regular drill** periods for **mathematics facts**. These should occasionally be timed. They may be either oral or written.

2. **Manipulatives, hand-held objects,** are basic to developing a relationship between the written problem and an understanding by the student of the problem solution. Manipulatives are both appropriate and essential at all grade levels. A majority of the manipulatives used in problems may be developed from material already available in the classroom or home. Measurements require measuring cups, rulers, and empty containers. Boxes and other similar items help the study of solid shapes. Construction paper, beads, buttons, beans are readily available to use for counting, fractions, sets, grouping, sequencing, and flat and solid shapes. **Manipulatives may extend to drawings.** For example, students may draw the shape of a figure when solving for area or perimeter. Have the students use colored pencil or crayons to show the figure's dimensions and flat surface. Then have them explain the logic of their answers.

3. **Dictation** strengthens comprehension. Dictate problems with answers for students to write on paper. (Five plus six equals eleven or $5 + 6 = 11$.) This will help them to develop vocabulary and spelling of mathematics terms. Problems may be written numerically or in words.

4. Keep a **log book of terms** with which the student is having difficulty. These may be identified from the *Introduction of Skills* or the *Mathematics Terms*. Quiz the student regularly until the term is mastered.

5. An **oral arithmetic bee** can be held in which problems are given orally and must be solved mentally. Selected LIFEPAC pages may be used for this exercise. Teach estimation and grouping of numbers for easier problem solving.

6. The student may create **number patterns** for others to solve.

When studying geometry,

7. Create 2- and 3-dimensional figures out of construction paper or cardboard.

8. Create figures that are congruent and/or similar. Form circles, squares, and rectangles from triangles. Try making octagons and pentagons from triangles, squares and rectangles. Cut figures into geometric shapes similar to jigsaw puzzles and then put back together.

When studying measurements,

9. Use groups of coins to show what combination of coins may be worth a certain amount of money.

10. Using local newspaper advertisements, have students make a collage of the items they could buy if they had $10.00 to spend. Prices should be included on the clippings.

11. Have students fill containers and then use a combination of measurers such as cup and quart, ounce and pound to determine quantity and weight.

12. Have the students measure their height, length of arms, legs and feet, the lengths around their heads, arms, wrists, and ankles.

When studying statistics,

13.   Gather data to form charts and graphs. Begin with gathering the data; then, decide how the data could be most effectively presented. Suggestions for data collection would be number of people living in each home, students eye color, shoe size, height, weight, food preferences.

14.   LIFEPAC **word problems** often reflect everyday experiences of the student. If a problem relates to the distance, rate and time of travel when a family visits friends or relatives, develop a similar problem the next time an actual trip is taken. Use all possible opportunities to translate word problems into similar real experiences.

ALTERNATE

T
E
S
T
S

Reproducible Tests
for use with the Mathematics
200 Teacher's Guide

MATHEMATICS

2 0 1

ALTERNATE LIFEPAC TEST

40 / 50

Name _____

Date _____

Score _____

MATHEMATICS 201: Alternate LIFEPAC TEST

1.   Match

thirty-six	13
sixty-three	33
sixty-six	63
thirteen	66
thirty-three	36

2.   Write in words

11 _____

7 _____

56 _____

30 _____

82 _____

3.   Write addition and subtraction facts.

7	8	9	5	4	15	7	9	13	11
+ 3	+ 4	+ 0	+ 6	+ 3	− 8	− 0	− 4	− 5	− 8

4.   Circle the tens' place.

4 6   1 3   8 4

5.   Write what comes next.

5, 4, 3, _____

6.   Add or subtract.

32	41	4	43	75	57
+ 7	+ 23	2	20	− 42	− 26
		+ 3	+ 15		

7.   Write the number

before.   after.

_____ 14   69 _____

_____ eighty   thirteen _____

8. Write a fact family.
(2 points)

4, 7, 11

____ + ____ = _____

____ + ____ = _____

____ − ____ = _____

____ − ____ = _____

9. Circle the symbol.

6 (+, −) 5 = 11

14 (+, −) 7 = 7

8 + 2 (=, ≠) 11

25 (>, <) 23

---

10. Read the story. Work the problem. (2 points)

Katie has five dimes.
Chad has four dimes.
How many dimes do
they have altogether? Answer:

11. Write the number sentence using symbols.

Thirteen minus four equals nine.   _____

Forty-seven is greater than thirty-seven.   _____

Sixteen is less than seventeen.   _____

Five plus zero is not equal to six.   _____

12. Match.

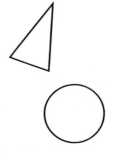

circle

rectangle

square

triangle

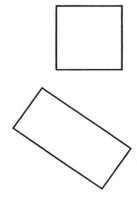

79

NOTES

MATHEMATICS

2 0 2

ALTERNATE
LIFEPAC TEST

$\dfrac{40}{50}$

Name _____

Date _____

Score _____

MATHEMATICS 202: Alternate LIFEPAC TEST

1. **Write the missing numbers.**

   187, ____, 189, ____, 191, 192, ____, 194, ____, ____

2. **Write addition and subtraction facts.**

   $5 + 6 =$ _____ $7 + 7 =$ _____ $12 - 7 =$ _____

   $8 + 3 =$ _____ $14 - 6 =$ _____ $8 - 0 =$ _____

3. **Write even or odd.**

   9 is _____.   16 is _____.   37 is _____.   64 is _____.

4. **When we count**

   by 10's, the number always ends with ____.

   by 5's, the number always ends with ____ or ____.

   by 2's, the number always ends with

   ____, ____, ____, ____, or ____.

5. **Write the answer.**   hours 12 minutes 60

   How many hours on a clock? _____

   How many minutes in a hour? _____

   The short hand tells the _____.

   The long hand tells the _____.

6.   Write the time.

_____ : _____ o'clock

7.   Subtract. Check. (3 points each)

```
    56              47
  −  3            − 25
  +              +
  ——————          ——————
```

8.   Write the numbers in columns. Add. Check. (3 points each)

5, 4, 10   31, 26, 2

_____   _____

+ _____   + _____

9.   Read the story. Work the problem. (2 points)

Brenda had nine cookies.
She gave three cookies to Janice.
How many cookies does
Brenda have now?   Answer:

10. Write how many. (2 points)

42¢

          dimes   nickels   pennies

= _____ + _____ + _____

11. Write.

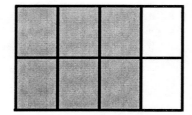

How many parts to the rectangle? _____

How many parts are shaded? _____

Write the shaded part as a fraction. _____

How many balloons in the set? _____

How many balloons are little? _____

Write the little balloons as a fraction. _____

MATHEMATICS

2 0 3

ALTERNATE
LIFEPAC TEST

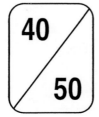

40 / 50

Name _____

Date _____

Score _____

MATHEMATICS 203: Alternate LIFEPAC TEST

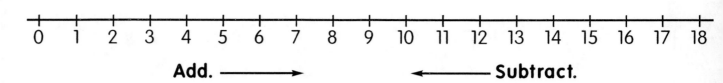

Add. ⟶   ⟵ Subtract.

1. Add and subtract.

$9 + 5 - 6 =$ _____ $13 - 7 + 3 =$ _____

2. Write how many. Write the value.

162 has _____ hundreds + _____ tens + _____ ones.

162 is equal to _____ + _____ + _____.

3. Add ones. Carry tens. Add tens.

☐   ☐   ☐   ☐
```
  34          57          26          28
+ 56        + 25        + 46        + 33
```

4. Measure.

_____ _____ inches

Are paper clips or inches
standard measurements?   _____

5. Write how many. (2 points)

 $6.29   dollars   dimes   nickels   pennies

_____   _____   _____   _____

6. Add or subtract. Write the signs. (2 points each)

$$26¢ + 32¢$$ $$67¢ - 45¢$$ $$\$5.27 + \$2.31$$ $$\$9.63 - \$4.22$$

7. Write A.M. or P.M.

I went to bed at 9:00 _____.   I ate breakfast at 7:30 _____.

8. Answer the questions. (3 points)

Is this a flat shape? _____
Use your ruler to complete the shape.

Name the shape. _____

Are flat shapes made from open or closed lines? _____

9. Count by 2's, 5's, and 10's.

6,   _____,   10,   12,   _____,   _____,   18

20,   25,   _____,   _____,   40,   45,   _____

110,   _____,   _____,   140,   _____,   160,   170

10. Round to the nearest 10.

33 _____   38 _____   12 _____

11. Write the numbers.

one hundred eleven   _____

one hundred fifty-six   _____

12. Write the number words.

160 _____

106 _____

13. Circle the fractions.

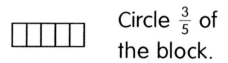 Circle $\frac{3}{5}$ of the block.

 Circle $\frac{2}{7}$ of the dogs.

14. Circle the correct sign.

48 (>, <) 63   17 (=, ≠) 8 + 9   13 = 8 (+, −) 5

MATHEMATICS

2 0 4

ALTERNATE LIFEPAC TEST

40 / 50

Name _____

Date _____

Score _____

MATHEMATICS 204: Alternate LIFEPAC TEST

1.   Write the missing numbers.

627,   _____,   _____,   630,   631

898,   899,   _____,   _____,   902

2.   Write the number word.

628   _____

3.   Write how many. Write the value.

903 has _____ hundreds + _____ tens + _____ ones.

903 is equal to _____ + _____ + _____.

4.   Change cents to coins. Show two examples. (2 points each)

73¢   =   _____ quarters _____ dimes _____ nickels _____ pennies

=   _____ quarters _____ dimes _____ nickels _____ pennies

5.   Add down. Add up.

$$
\begin{array}{r} 361 \\ + 234 \\ \hline \end{array}
\qquad
\begin{array}{r} 41 \\ 36 \\ + 20 \\ \hline \end{array}
\qquad
\begin{array}{r} \square \\ 27 \\ + 46 \\ \hline \end{array}
\qquad
\begin{array}{r} 27 \\ + 46 \\ \hline \square \end{array}
$$

6. **Subtract.** Check. Add the take-away number. (2 points each)

$$78$$
$$-\ 25$$

$$+\ \_\_\_\_$$

$$847$$
$$-\ 326$$

$$+\ \_\_\_\_$$

$$549$$
$$-\ 127$$

$$+\ \_\_\_\_$$

7. **Write the standard measurements.**

_____ inches = 1 yard   _____ inches = 1 foot

_____ feet = 1 yard

8. **What measurement would you use**
to measure the length of a driveway? _____

9. **Draw a circle around the solid shapes.**

   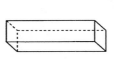

10. Read the story. Work the problem. (4 points)

A toy car costs 73¢.   ¢
We gave the storekeeper 7 dimes   −   ¢
                    and 1 nickel or _____¢.   _____
We paid the storekeeper more than 73¢.   ¢
He will give us change.

What change will the storekeeper give us? _____

91

11. Round to the nearest 10.

12 _____   69 _____   93 _____   48 _____

12. Write the numbers in number order. (4 points)

847   147   747   347   647   247   547   947   447

_____ _____ _____ _____ _____ _____ _____ _____ _____

13. Read the story. Work the problem. (2 points)

Kelly walked 8 blocks to the
store on Tuesday.
She walked 3 blocks to the
park on Wednesday.
How much farther did she
walk on Tuesday than
on Wednesday?   Answer:

14. Use your calendar. Write today's date. (4 points)

_____   _____   _____, _____
   day of week   month   date   year

MATHEMATICS

2 0 5

ALTERNATE
LIFEPAC TEST

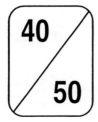

Name _____

Date _____

Score _____

MATHEMATICS 205: Alternate LIFEPAC TEST

1. **Write the facts.** Write > or < on the line. (6 points)

   9 + 3 (>, <) 6 + 5   14 − 7 (>, <) 15 − 6

   _____ ____ _____   _____ ____ _____

Smile!

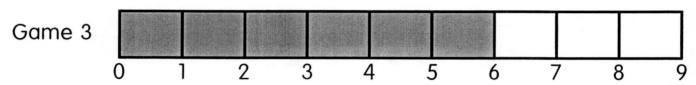

Game 3

2. How many matches were made in Game 3? _____

   The information posted to the graph is _____ .

   This is a _____ graph.

3. **Write the missing numbers.** Tell the pattern.

   2,   4,   ____,   8,   ____,   ____,   14   _____

4. This object is soft. It is round like a sphere.
   It has a good smell. It is heavy.

   What is it? _____

5. **Count by 3's.** Circle the numbers. (2 points)

   1   2   3   4   5   6   7   8   9   10   11   12

6. **Write ones, tens, or hundreds.** Tell the value.

   637 has a 3 in the _____ place.

   The value of 3 is _____ .

7. Write the largest and smallest number.

5, 1, 8   largest _____   smallest _____

8. Zero has no value. Zero is called a _____.

9. Add.

$$\frac{4}{7}$$
$$+\frac{1}{7}$$
_____

$$\frac{3}{6}$$
$$+\frac{2}{6}$$
_____

$$\frac{2}{8}$$
$$+\frac{5}{8}$$
_____

$$\frac{1}{3}$$
$$+\frac{1}{3}$$
_____

10. Write the ordinal number for the cardinal number.

three _____   thirteen _____

11. Write the answer.

How many in a dozen?   _____

12. Draw a line on the thermometer.

Show the temperature that measures
a pot of boiling water.

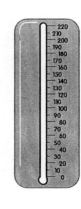

13. Write the answer on the lines. (1 point)

dollars	quarters	dimes	nickels	pennies
$3.69	_____	_____	_____	_____	_____

14. Add or subtract.

$3.46	$5.22	$2.31	$8.43	$9.64
+ $1.23	+ $4.63	+ $3.25	− $4.13	− $2.12

35	53	86	57	78
+ 2	+ 25	− 6	− 24	− 36

41	16	357	789	817
20	32	− 215	− 362	− 305
+ 18	+ 21			

☐	☐		☐	☐
26	37	346	535	243
+ 8	+ 5	+ 242	+ 318	+ 237

MATHEMATICS

2 0 6

ALTERNATE
LIFEPAC TEST

40 / 50

Name _____

Date _____

Score _____

MATHEMATICS 206: Alternate LIFEPAC TEST

1.   Write the time.

____:____   ____:____

2.   Draw the hands.

5:47   10:18

3.   Write the answer.

_____ inches = 1 foot   _____ ounces = 1 pound

What measurement would you use
to measure the weight of a bag of apples? _____

4.   Subtract. (2 points each)

☐☐   ☐☐   ☐☐   ☐☐
5 3   7 4   8 5   6 2
− 2 7   − 2 7   − 2 9   − 4 6

☐☐   ☐☐   ☐☐   ☐☐
5 8   6 2   9 3   8 4
− 2 9   − 3 8   − 5 7   − 2 6

5.   Write how many. Write the value. (2 points)

308 = _____ hundreds + _____ tens + _____ ones.

= _____ + _____ + _____

Write in words. 308

_____

98

6.

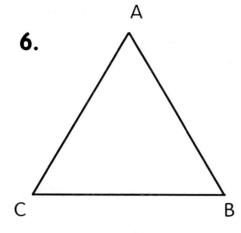

Measure from A to B. _____ linear inches

Measure from B to C. _____ linear inches

Measure from C to A. _____ linear inches

The perimeter is _____ linear inches

7. Circle the even numbers. (2 points)

1   2   3   4   5   6   7   8   9   10

8. Add or subtract.

$$+ \frac{\frac{3}{5}}{\frac{1}{5}} \qquad + \frac{\frac{2}{12}}{\frac{5}{12}} \qquad + \frac{\frac{3}{9}}{\frac{4}{9}} \qquad - \frac{\frac{7}{8}}{\frac{3}{8}} \qquad - \frac{\frac{6}{7}}{\frac{4}{7}} \qquad - \frac{\frac{2}{3}}{\frac{1}{3}}$$

9. Read the story. Work the problem.

Jeffry wanted to buy a dinosaur book.
The book cost $3.34.
Jeffry had 2 dollars, 5 quarters, and 1 dime.

How much money did Jeffry have? _____

Did he have enough money to buy the book? _____

10. Measure.

_____ _____ inches

11. Write a fact family.
(2points)

2, 9, 11

12. Add.

☐
357
+ 138

☐
536
+ 225

13. Write the numbers in number order. (4 points)

310   578   425   487   304   504   587   452

_____   _____   _____   _____   _____   _____   _____   _____

14. Name the shape that does not belong.

_____

MATHEMATICS

2 0 7

ALTERNATE
LIFEPAC TEST

40 / 50

Name _____

Date _____

Score _____

MATHEMATICS 207: Alternate LIFEPAC TEST

1. Write the fractions in words.

$\frac{3}{7}$ _____ $\frac{2}{3}$ _____

2. Add or subtract.

$$\begin{array}{r} 32 \\ 43 \\ +\ 21 \\ \hline \end{array} \qquad \begin{array}{r} 235 \\ +\ 462 \\ \hline \end{array} \qquad \begin{array}{r} \square \\ 345 \\ +\ 235 \\ \hline \end{array} \qquad \begin{array}{r} \square \\ 463 \\ +\ 281 \\ \hline \end{array}$$

$$\begin{array}{r} 67 \\ -\ 42 \\ \hline \end{array} \qquad \begin{array}{r} 537 \\ -\ 215 \\ \hline \end{array} \qquad \begin{array}{r} \square\square \\ 82 \\ -\ 38 \\ \hline \end{array} \qquad \begin{array}{r} \square\square \\ 74 \\ -\ 37 \\ \hline \end{array}$$

3. Find the pattern. Write what comes next.

Tell the pattern.

$3 + 0 = 3 \qquad 3 + 1 = 4 \qquad 3 + 2 = 5$ _____ _____

$20 , \qquad\quad 30 , \qquad\quad 40 ,$ _____ _____

4. Add or subtract.

$$+\ \begin{array}{c} \frac{4}{8} \\ \frac{2}{8} \\ \hline \end{array} \qquad\qquad +\ \begin{array}{c} \frac{3}{9} \\ \frac{4}{9} \\ \hline \end{array} \qquad\qquad -\ \begin{array}{c} \frac{8}{15} \\ \frac{3}{15} \\ \hline \end{array} \qquad\qquad -\ \begin{array}{c} \frac{7}{12} \\ \frac{5}{12} \\ \hline \end{array}$$

Write the first problem in words.

_____

5. **Read the story.** Work the problem. (2 points each)

Mary sold 7 boxes of cookies on Monday,
6 on Tuesday, and 5 on Wednesday.
How many boxes did she sell altogether?   _____

Curt ate $\frac{1}{5}$ of a box of cereal.
Jess ate $\frac{2}{5}$ of a box of cereal.
How much cereal did they eat altogether?   _____

The crayons cost 73¢.
Ken paid 7 dimes and one nickel.
What was his change? Write the answer in coins.   _____

6. **Number the months in order.** (4 points)

_____	_____	_____	_____	_____	_____
February	April	March	January	July	November

_____	_____	_____	_____	_____	_____
June	September	May	October	August	December

7. **Write the number word.**

640 _____

8. **Write how many.** Write the value. (2 points)

	hundreds		tens		ones
360 =	_____	+	_____	+	_____
=	_____	+	_____	+	_____

103

9. Write the answer.

When we count by 10's, the numbers end in _____.

When we count by 5's, the numbers end in _____ or _____.

The distance around the
outside of a flat shape is the _____.

If you have 24 buttons,
you have close to _____ buttons.

Are there more pages or chapters in a book? _____

10. Write the standard measurements.

_____ inches = 1 foot _____ feet = 1 yard _____ ounces = 1 pound

_____ minutes = 1 hour _____ days = 1 week

11. Read the graph. Write the temperature for Friday.

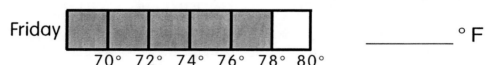

Friday   _____ °F

70° 72° 74° 76° 78° 80°

12. Draw the hands on the clocks.

Write morning or afternoon on the line.

10:25 A.M.   3:42 P.M.   7:23 P.M.

_____   _____   _____

MATHEMATICS

208

ALTERNATE LIFEPAC TEST

40 / 50

Name _____

Date _____

Score _____

MATHEMATICS 208: Alternate LIFEPAC TEST

1. **Write the missing number in the sequence.**

    _____,   9,   8   63, _____,   65

    310,   312, _____   501, _____,   499

2. **Write the answer.**

    $18 - 7 + 3 =$ _____

    $22 + 4 - 5 =$ _____

    $13 + 5 - 0 =$ _____

    $18 - 9 - 4 =$ _____

3. **Write the family facts.**
    (2 points)

    7, 9, 16

4. **Complete the number sentences.**

    $+, -$ $=, \neq$ $>, <$

    5 ___ $4 = 9$ $5 + 2$ ___ $14 - 6$ $18 - 9$ ___ $5 + 5$

    12 ___ $4 = 8$ $15 - 9$ ___ $7 - 3$ $7 + 6$ ___ $14 - 6$

5. **Write the fewest number of dollars and coins possible.** (2 points)

    $2.63   ____ dollars ____ quarters ____ dimes ____ nickels ____ pennies

6. **Tell the order of the shapes.**

    The star is the _____ shape.

    The circle is the _____ shape.

7. Draw a rectangle. Write the perimeter.   (2 points)

length - 3 inches

width - 2 inches

perimeter = _____

8. Circle $\frac{4}{7}$.

$\frac{4}{7}$ of set of bows is _____ bows.

9. Add or subtract.

$$\begin{array}{r} \frac{2}{6} \\ + \frac{3}{6} \\ \hline \end{array} \qquad \begin{array}{r} \frac{1}{7} \\ + \frac{5}{7} \\ \hline \end{array} \qquad \begin{array}{r} \frac{9}{12} \\ - \frac{3}{12} \\ \hline \end{array} \qquad \begin{array}{r} \frac{8}{16} \\ - \frac{2}{16} \\ \hline \end{array}$$

10. We say that

62 people are close to _____ people.

87 miles are close to _____ miles.

11. Write the largest and smallest number.

7 2 4   largest _____   smallest _____

12. Write the directions.

north   south
east   west

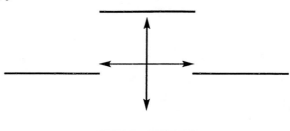

13. Write the answer.

_____ cups = 1 pint   _____ pints = 1 quart

_____ quarts = 1 gallon

What would you use to measure milk for your cereal? _____

14. Add.

☐
$4.35
+ $2.27

☐
$3.46
+ $3.26

☐☐
375
+ 465

☐☐
527
+ 296

16. Add. Check. (2 points)

☐
37
+ 45

_____
37
+ 45
☐

17. Subtract. Check. (4 points)

☐☐
72
− 48
+ _____

679
− 215
+ _____

MATHEMATICS

2 0 9

ALTERNATE LIFEPAC TEST

Name _____

Date _____

Score _____

MATHEMATICS 209: Alternate LIFEPAC TEST

1. **Measure the rectangle.** Label your answers.

   length _____

   width _____

   perimeter _____   area _____

2. **Write how many.** Write the value. (2 points)

   835 = _____ hundreds + _____ tens + _____ ones.

   = _____   + _____   + _____

3. **Circle the numbers in the tens' place.**

   73   609

4. **Write north, south, east, or west.**

                           ↓

   _____   _____   _____   _____

5. **Complete the bar graph.**
   Show the spinner stopped at 5, twelve times.

   _5_

   0   5   10   15   20

6. **Use your ruler.** Draw a line.

   $1\frac{1}{2}$ inches

7.   Draw the time on the clock. Write A.M. or P.M.

I arrived home at 10:33 in the morning.   _____

8.   Change coins to cents.

1 quarters, 4 nickels, 3 pennies

_____ ¢ quarters

_____ ¢ nickels

+ _____ ¢ pennies

_____ ¢ total cents

9.   Write the answer.

8 + 7 − 6 = _____

7 − 3 + 8 = _____

37 − 6 + 4 = _____

53 + 6 − 7 = _____

10. Write the answer.

When counting by 2's, 6 is the _____ number.

Round 59 to the nearest 10. _____

11. Write the numbers for the number words.

seventy-three   _____   five hundred fourteen _____

two-thirds   _____   four-ninths   _____

12. Write the number words.

540 _____

906 _____

$\frac{2}{6}$ _____ $\frac{4}{7}$ _____

13. Write the operation symbols.

$>, <$ $=, \neq$ $+, -$

7 + 4 _____ 13   18 − 9 _____ 5   12 = 7 _____ 5

6 _____ 12 − 5   13 _____ 6 + 8   9 _____ 2 = 7

14. Add. Write even or odd on the line.

12   +   5   =   _____

_____ + _____ = _____

15. Add or subtract.

$\square$	$\square\square$	$\square\square$	$\square\square$		
53	56	932	368	$\frac{3}{5}$	$\frac{7}{12}$
26	− 28	− 427	+ 254	$+ \frac{1}{5}$	$- \frac{4}{12}$
+ 35					

MATHEMATICS

210

ALTERNATE LIFEPAC TEST

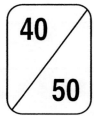

40 / 50

Name _____

Date _____

Score _____

MATHEMATICS 210: Alternate LIFEPAC TEST

1. Round to the nearest 100.

389 _____   827 _____   650 _____

2. Read the problem. Write the answer. (2 points each)

There were 643 children enrolled in the school.
425 children ate their lunch at school.
How many children did not each lunch at school?   _____

Lisa poured 1 quart of water into the gallon container.
How many more quarts of water did Lisa need
to pour to fill the container?   _____

3. Show three sets of coins that equal these cents. (3 points)

	quarters	dimes	nickels	pennies
91¢	_____	_____	_____	_____
	_____	_____	_____	_____
	_____	_____	_____	_____

4. Write even or odd.

odd + odd = _____   even + odd = _____

5. Write in number words.

12 _____

627 _____

$5.07 _____

$2.43 _____

6. Write in number symbols.

sixty _____   two hundred eighty three _____

four dollars and twenty-one cents _____

eight dollars and fifty cents _____

7. Write how many. Write the value.

529 = _____ hundreds + _____ tens + _____ ones.

= _____   + _____   + _____

8. Circle the eighth apple.

9. Draw hands on the dial clock.
Show the same time as the digital clock.

8:30 ● A.M.
         P.M.

10. Show a temperature of 73° on June 3.

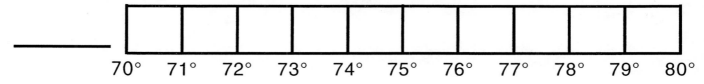

70° 71° 72° 73° 74° 75° 76° 77° 78° 79° 80°

11. Measure the rectangle. Label your answers.

length _____

width _____

perimeter _____   area _____

12. Color. Write the fractions. Add. (4 points)

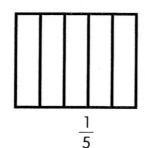

$\dfrac{1}{5}$

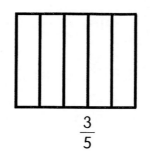

$\dfrac{3}{5}$

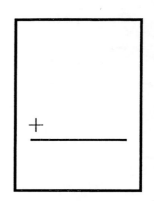

$+$ _____
_____

13. Write the symbol.

Make the number sentences true. $+$, $-$, $=$ (2 points each)

63 ____ 5 ____ 68   15 ____ 9 ____ 6

14. Write what comes next.

$6.37, $6.38, $6.39, _____ $\dfrac{1}{8}$, $\dfrac{2}{8}$, $\dfrac{3}{8}$, _____

15. Add or subtract.

45	257	65	546	$3.47	$8.42
26	+ 384	− 28	− 208	+ $5.26	− $3.28
+ 51					

ANSWER KEYS

Part One

1.1 0 1 2 3 4 5 6 7 8 9 10

1.2 zero one two three four
five six seven eight nine ten

1.3 4 3 6 5 0
9 2 7 10 8 1

1.4 11 12 13 14 15 16 17 18 19 20

1.5 eleven twelve thirteen fourteen
fifteen sixteen seventeen
eighteen nineteen twenty

1.6
b	c
t	f
m	s
r	g
d	o
e	p
q	k
n	a
l	i
h	j

1.7
9	16	11	9	5	13	7	5	10
1	8	4	11	14	6	8	10	7
13	9	7	12	11	15	14	7	3
10	13	10	16	10	9	6	14	10
4	11	14	17	11	2	2	15	12
8	12	7	6	10	15	7	10	8
13	16	11	3	6	11	9	18	8
8	8	11	5	15	3	4	13	9
12	9	4	12	5	7	6	9	17
8	5	9	12	12	14	6	13	10

1.8
10	20	30	40	50
60	70	80	90	100

1.9 ten twenty thirty forty fifty sixty
seventy eighty ninety one hundred

1.10
16	forty-five
31	sixty
67	seventy-nine
85	thirteen
49	eighty-one
11	thirty-six
70	fifty-four
93	one hundred

Part Two

2.1
5	9	6	3	0	4	1	3	2
3	8	4	4	9	1	4	0	5
1	7	6	6	6	8	5	8	1
1	6	0	2	3	0	8	5	1
5	5	5	2	1	8	4	0	7
7	9	6	3	2	5	3	4	6
2	8	5	6	5	9	9	7	2
8	2	4	7	9	4	3	2	9
8	9	0	7	1	0	7	9	6
0	4	7	7	1	0	2	3	3

2.2
(2)7	(4)5	(8)3	(6)1
(1)7	(5)8	(1)1	(9)6
1(2)	7(8)	3(9)	4(6)
8(9)	1(5)	2(2)	7(0)

2.3
(1)6	(2)6	(5)9	(7)0
(9)8	(4)1	(3)7	(6)2

2.4
(twenty)seven	(thirty)five
(sixty)one	(eighty)nine
(forty)four	(ninety)six
(seventy)two	(fifty)three

2.5
1	7	17
2	3	23
2	7	27
0	4	4
4	3	43
2	8	28
4	6	46

2.6
49	35	55	67	29	75
37	79	68	98	62	86

2.7
88	56	48	86	97	52
69	47	66	84	95	79

2.8
46	32	54	28	65	70
33	75	62	60	93	47

2.9
65	53	14	63	81	82
46	16	44	72	21	54

Part Three

3.1
15	85	12
22	10	99
74	19	49
4	62	36

3.2	23	13	100
	52	27	64
	90	52	20
	32	40	77

3.3	79	34	16
	44	99	49
	28	4	22
	20	82	91

3.4 thirteen   ten
     twenty-one   fifty-two
     sixty-two   seventy
     seventy-nine   forty

3.5 forty-five   sixty-seven
     eighty-two   forty
     thirteen   ninety-four
     eight   seventeen

3.6 twenty
     forty-seven
     ninety-one
     sixty-eight
     ten
     seventy-four
     thirty-six
     ninety-nine

3.7 +   −
     =   −
     −   +
     −   =
     +/−   +
     =   =
     +   −
     −   +
     =   =
     +   −

3.8 =   ≠
     ≠   =
     =   ≠
     ≠   =
     ≠   ≠
     ≠   ≠
     =   =
     ≠   ≠

3.9 12, 7, 9, 11, 6, 8, 10, 5
     9, 12, 13, 11, 14, 8, 10, 15

3.10 >   <
      <   >
      >   >
      >   >
      >   <
      <   <
      >   >
      >   >

3.11 13, 14, 16, 17, 18, 20
      38, 39, 40, 42, 43, 44
      74, 76, 77, 79, 80, 81

3.12 $6 + 3 = 9$
      $8 − 4 \neq 3$
      $12 > 11$
      $54 < 56$
      $13 − 7 = 6$
      $4 > 0$
      $6 + 2 \neq 7$
      $81 < 95$
      $3 + 5 > 4 + 2$
      $26 − 4 < 19 + 8$

Part Four

4.1	8	9, 14	7, 8, 15
	8	5, 14	8, 7, 15
	6	5, 9	15, 7, 8
	2	9, 5	15, 8, 7

4.2 Suggested Answers:

0	1	4	6	7	8
$+6$	$+5$	$+2$	-0	-1	-2
6	6	6	6	6	6

4.3	3, 9, 12	2, 7, 9	4, 7, 11
	9, 3, 12	7, 2, 9	7, 4, 11
	12, 3, 9	9, 2, 7	11, 4, 7
	12, 9, 3	9, 7, 2	11, 7, 4
	3, 5, 8	8, 9, 17	6, 7, 13
	5, 3, 8	9, 8, 17	7, 6, 13
	8, 3, 5	17, 8, 9	13, 6, 7
	8, 5, 3	17, 9, 8	13, 7, 6

4.4 Suggested Answers:

4, 6, 10	5, 9, 14	0, 5, 5
4, 6, 10	5, 9, 14	0, 5, 5
6, 4, 10	9, 5, 14	5, 0, 5
10, 4, 6	14, 5, 9	5, 0, 5
10, 6, 4	14, 9, 5	5, 5, 0

4.5

$$\begin{array}{r} 6 \\ + 7 \\ \hline 13 \end{array}$$ 13 pets

$$\begin{array}{r} 3 \\ + 9 \\ \hline 12 \end{array}$$ 12 sisters

$$\begin{array}{r} 6 \\ + 8 \\ \hline 14 \end{array}$$ 14 people

4.6

$$\begin{array}{r} 4 \\ + 3 \\ \hline 7 \end{array}$$

4 < 5

$$\begin{array}{r} 14 \\ - 9 \\ \hline 5 \end{array}$$

thirty-four

$$\begin{array}{r} 76 \\ - 40 \\ \hline 36 \end{array}$$

39

17

☺ or ☺☺☺

4.7

6	8	9	9	8	10
9	6	8	7	9	10
98	57	83	79	88	

4.8

no

Part Five

5.1

four	twenty-six
ten	forty-two
thirty-five	fourteen
seventy-nine	sixty-four

5.2

forty	forty-one
sixteen	seventeen
seventy-two	seventy-three
ninety-eight	ninety-nine

5.3

fourteen — 14
fifty-nine — 59
forty-one — 41
nineteen — 19
forty-nine — 49

33 — thirty-three
63 — sixty-three
36 — thirty-six
60 — sixty
66 — sixty-six

5.4

7	13	12
10	6	15
17	10	8
8	16	16
12	12	9
7	3	4
9	9	9
12	14	2

5.5

4	9	2
6	4	4
8	8	5
3	7	5
4	2	0
2	9	7
9	3	6
5	1	4

5.6

7	15	9	10	13	12	9	14
16	4	5	18	12	4	7	8
6	10	11	10	12	14	1	11

5.7

1	6	5	0	3	9	5	9
3	8	6	8	2	8	9	6
9	0	4	4	9	7	0	0

5.8
=	=
−	≠
≠	−
+	≠
=	+
−	−
≠	≠
=	=

5.9
>	<
<	>
<	<
>	>

5.10 Teacher Check

Part One

1.1 Teacher Check

1.2
60	61	62	63	64
65	66	67	68	69

130	131	132	133	134
135	136	137	138	139

1.3

	101		103		105	106		108	
110	111	112		114	115		117		119
120		122	123		125	126		128	129
	131		133	134			137	138	
140	141	142			145	146			149
150			153	154	155		157	158	
	161	162		164		166	167		169
170	171	172	173		175			178	
180		182		184		186	187	188	
190			193		195	196	197		199

1.4 one hundred one — 101
one hundred twenty-three — 123
one hundred fifteen — 115
one hundred forty-nine — 149
one hundred eighty-three — 183
one hundred four — 104
one hundred seventy — 170
two hundred — 200

104
115
170
200
123
183
101
149

101
104
115
123
149
170
183
200

1.5
7	10	3
6	13	13
4	17	11
8	2	9
12	9	15
13	5	5
10	9	10
16	12	5
4	7	10
5	5	7
11	14	13
10	3	6
18	13	9
8	11	10
3	6	6
13	9	6
12	12	15
8	9	7
4	8	12
8	6	9
10	7	15
11	13	9
15	11	2
12	17	11
12	8	10
11	8	16
1	8	14
4	7	14
7	16	10
11	14	14

1.6 odd
even
odd
even
odd
even
odd
even
odd
even

even	even	odd
odd	odd	even

1.7 Teacher Check
0
0, 5
0, 2, 4, 6, 8

Part Two

2.1
2	4	1
7	0	3
2	5	8
0	2	3

4	0	7
4	6	5
1	6	0
0	7	8
8	4	1
3	2	4
8	2	1
4	5	2
9	9	7
7	0	5
6	2	8
5	5	5
7	1	5
1	9	6
0	3	9
9	0	6
2	1	3
3	9	7
1	7	4
6	8	8
7	4	3
3	5	8
0	3	1
6	4	9
9	9	8
6	6	2

2.2

3, 4, 7	4, 6, 110
3, 4, 7	4, 6, 10
4, 3, 7	6, 4, 10
7, 3, 4	10, 4, 6
7, 4, 3	10, 6, 4

1, 6, 7	3, 8, 11
1, 6, 7	3, 8, 11
6, 1, 7	8, 3, 11
7, 1, 6	11, 3, 8
7, 6, 1	11, 8, 3

5, 8, 13	0, 5, 5
5, 8, 13	0, 5, 5
8, 5, 13	5, 0, 5
13, 5, 8	5, 0, 5
13, 8, 5	5, 5, 0

8, 9, 17	2, 5, 7
8, 9, 17	2, 5, 7
9, 8, 17	5, 2, 7

17, 8, 9	7, 2, 5
17, 9, 8	7, 5, 2

2.3 Teacher Check

2.4 4, 35, 4:35

2.5

10	25	45
40	15	55

2.6

8:00	4:15	7:35	11:25
9:50	6:40	2:05	3:55

2.7 4:30
7, 8

Part Three

3.1

123	111	99
155	163	136
179	190	117
144	103	178

3.2

116	177	104
130	149	100
137	160	151
110	182	168

3.3

108	130	137
179	111	176
114	154	190
167	199	109

3.4 6⑦ 4③ 1① ⑤ 9⑥ ①

3.5 ②4 ③2 ⑧5 ①0 ①9 ④6

3.6

14	5	20	3
13	11	2	2
+ 2	+ 23	+ 14	+ 64
29	39	36	69

43	5	24	4
2	2	10	41
+ 10	+ 21	+ 13	+ 23
55	28	47	68

3.7

78	19	29	47	87	56
96	98	86	57	95	79
12	16	11	13	6	9
108	99	97	69	87	99
77	15	22	82	41	55
81	63	72	25	41	37

3.8	15	7	66	18	79	39
	77	78	83	79	49	77
	15	12	10	14	11	14
	98	87	99	75	97	73

3.9	1	2	8	5	1	7
	74	12	43	54	30	81
	65	14	16	40	19	24
	14	15	33	20	51	21

3.10 third
ninth
fifth
second
eighth
tenth
first
fourth
sixth
seventh

3.11	9	3	15	13
	6	1	12	16
	0	8	17	18
	2	7	14	10
	4	5	11	

3.12 +, −   =, ≠   >, <

3.13 nine   nine
Five   seven

3.14 minus   plus
plus   minus
equals
is not equal to
less than
greater than

Part Four

4.1	=	>
	≠	<
	≠	<
	=	>

4.2	136	137	138	139	
			140	141	142
	39	56	63	98	
			137	175	182

4.3	104	103	102	101	
			100	99	98
	200	191	162	126	
			114	19	5

4.4 2
1
$\frac{1}{2}$ $\frac{1}{2}$
5
2
$\frac{2}{5}$ $\frac{3}{5}$
3
2
$\frac{2}{3}$ $\frac{1}{3}$
4
3
$\frac{3}{4}$ $\frac{1}{4}$
4
1
$\frac{1}{4}$ $\frac{3}{4}$

4.5 6
4
$\frac{4}{6}$
$\frac{2}{6}$

4.6 5
1
$\frac{1}{5}$ $\frac{4}{5}$
3
2
$\frac{2}{3}$ $\frac{1}{3}$
6
4
$\frac{4}{6}$ $\frac{2}{6}$
5
2
$\frac{2}{5}$ $\frac{3}{5}$
6
1
$\frac{1}{6}$ $\frac{5}{6}$

4.7 5
3
$\frac{3}{5}$
$\frac{2}{5}$

4.8 triangle   square

$\frac{1}{2}$ △ △ $\frac{1}{2}$ $\frac{5}{8}$ ⊞ ⊟ $\frac{3}{8}$

rectangle   balloons

$\frac{2}{5}$ ▯ ▯ $\frac{3}{5}$ $\frac{4}{6}$ 🎈 🎈 $\frac{2}{6}$

flowers   smiling faces

$\frac{1}{4}$ 🌼 🌼 $\frac{3}{4}$ $\frac{3}{7}$ 🙂 🙂 $\frac{4}{7}$

4.9 10, 1

4.10 2, 1
40, 4
30, 6

4.11 Suggested Answers:

6	1	4
3	1	
1	1	1
	1	4
7		4
9	1	3
4	1	2
5	1	

4.12 75¢—seventy-five cents—
7 dimes 1 nickel
30¢—thirty cents—
6 nickels
82¢—eighty-two cents—
8 dimes 2 pennies
56¢—fifty-six cents—
5 dimes 1 nickel 1 penny
94¢—ninety-four cents—
8 dimes 2 nickels 4 pennies
13¢—thirteen cents—
2 nickels 3 pennies

4.13 68¢   79¢   72¢   76¢   85¢   89¢
43¢   12¢   24¢   11¢   3¢   33¢

4.14

square
triangle
oval
rectangle
circle

Part Five

5.1
$$\begin{array}{r} 5 \\ -\ 2 \\ \hline 3 \end{array}$$ 3 hours

$$\begin{array}{r} 7 \\ -\ 5 \\ \hline 2 \end{array}$$ 2 people

$$\begin{array}{r} 15 \\ -\ 9 \\ \hline 6 \end{array}$$ 6 books

$$\begin{array}{r} 25 \\ -\ 15 \\ \hline 10 \end{array}$$ 10 minutes

5.2
$$\begin{array}{r} 6 \\ -\ 4 \\ \hline 2 \end{array}$$ 2 books

$$\begin{array}{r} 3 \\ +\ 5 \\ \hline 8 \end{array}$$ 8 cookies

$$\begin{array}{r} 9 \\ +\ 8 \\ \hline 17 \end{array}$$ 17 fish

$$\begin{array}{r} 12 \\ -\ 3 \\ \hline 9 \end{array}$$ 9 people

$$\begin{array}{r} 6 \\ +\ 5 \\ \hline 11 \end{array}$$ 11 birds

$$\begin{array}{r} 3 \\ +\ 4 \\ \hline 7 \end{array}$$ 7 balls

126

5.3

+			
	7	5	4
	10	8	7
	11	9	8

+			
	11	10	9
	12	11	10
	5	4	3

+			
	12	6	5
	14	8	7
	10	4	3

5.4   7, 1, 3, 2, 5, 4
       5, 9, 4, 8, 7, 6
       10, 7, 6, 8, 0, 9

5.5   10:15   7:55   1:30   4:40

5.6   **Teacher Check**
       Even - 2, 4, 6, 8, 10, 12, 14, 16,
               18, 20, 22, 24, 26, 28, 30

       5's - 5, 10, 15, 20, 25, 30

       10's - 10, 20, 30

5.7   75   69   78   43   23   49
       22   31   33   89   95   59

Part One

1.1
12, 9, 11   11
11, 7, 15   15
6, 1, 8   8
17, 9, 9   9

1..2
8   12
7   10
17   9
9   8
14   8

nine
seventeen
seven

1.3
12 + 2 − 3 = 11 cars
8 − 4 + 3 = 7 dimes
5 + 3 + 8 = 16 blocks
18 − 4 − 5 = 9 cards

1.4
32 — one hundred fifty-six
12 — thirty-two
156 — one hundred sixty five
132 — twelve
165 — one hundred thirty-two
102 — ninety-two
92 — one hundred two

1.5
13②   ⑤   17⓪   5⑥
10⑤   ①3   ⑧4   17⑤
①51   ①80   ①04   ②00

1.6
1, 2, 3
100, 20, 3

1, 0, 7
100, 0, 7

1, 4, 6
100, 40, 6

1.7
1, 5, 0
100, 50, 0

0, 3, 2
0, 30, 2

0, 0, 4
0, 0, 4

1.8
68, 70   45, 47   167, 169
31, 33   108, 110   1, 3
119, 121   152, 154   8, 10
148, 150   166, 168   189, 191

1.9
1 18 41 71 100 132 158
1 10 1 1 100 100 100

1.10
$$3 + 4 = 7 \qquad 43 + 26 = 69 \qquad 15 - 9 = 6 \qquad 85 - 63 = 22$$
6 > 4
18 ≠ 81

1.11
six   fourteen   forty-nine
one hundred eighty-two
Four plus five equals nine.

1.12   O N E   H U N D R E D

Part Two

2.1
①1 , 1, 1
①3 , 1, 3
①0 , 1, 0
①2 , 1, 2

2.2
All carried numbers are 1.
2 3 5 8 0 1

2.3
All carried numbers are 1.
37 20 73 91 84 90

2.4
①0 ①6 ①2 ①2 ①0 ①2 ①4

2.5
All carried numbers are 1.
0 7 1 0 4 4 2

2.6
All carried numbers are 1.
91 23 40 62 75 82 82
73 30 64 22 42 92 83

2.7   Teacher Check.

2.8   9 inches - Everyone understands inches.

2.9   4 $1\frac{1}{2}$ $2\frac{1}{2}$

2.10 19

2.11
12 54 73 21 25 19
72 30 45 53 81 72

2.12
2 + 3 = 5   4 + 6 = 10
3 + 2 = 5   6 + 4 = 10
5 − 2 = 3   10 − 4 = 6
5 − 3 = 2   10 − 6 = 4

$$7 + 8 = 15$$
$$8 + 7 = 15$$
$$15 - 7 = 8$$
$$15 - 8 = 7$$

$$4 + 9 = 13$$
$$9 + 4 = 13$$
$$13 - 4 = 9$$
$$13 - 9 = 4$$

2.13

15	153
63	102
99	111

2.14

27	54	23	23	26	41
61	33	20	60	31	24

2.15

8	9	6
2	8	9
15	7	7
8	7	3

2.16
eighteen
forty-seven
one hundred thirty-eight
one hundred nine
thirty-two
two hundred

2.17 $3 + 3 = 6$

148

99

$7 - 4 = 3$

sixth

3.3

$2.98

$1.75
+ $1.23
$2.98

46¢

67¢
− 21¢
46¢

3.4 10, 20, 25, 30, 40, 45

3.5

125, 127	138, 140	111, 113
13, 15	48, 50	169, 171

3.6 4, 8, 10, 12, 14, 16, 18

3.7

<	>	<
>	<	>

3.8
twenty-six
one hundred twenty-nine

thirteen
one hundred six

seventy-nine
one hundred twelve

3.9

15	9	16	11	56	95
8	8	21	90	53	32

3.10 All carried numbers are 1.

70	62	64	80	42
80	82	45	80	73
140	100	144	124	153

3.11 no, yes, triangle

3.12 no, yes, rectangle

3.13 no, yes, square

3.14 no, yes, circle

3.15 They lie flat on a surface.

3.16 Teacher Check

Part Three

3.1

1	3	1	
4	2		2
	6	1	3
7	3		4
8	4	1	4
1	5		3

3.2

36¢	22¢	$3.67	$3.15
48¢	17¢	$7.87	$2.21

Part Four

4.1

7	13	13	2	6	15
7	9	12	5	14	10

15	10	11
11	5	7
11	6	17

4	1	6	8	5	5
0	9	8	0	5	4

9	6	0
3	2	6
3	8	1

4.2 12 hours
12 hours
24 hours

4.3 A.M., P.M., P.M., A.M., P.M., P.M.

4.4 Teacher Check

4.5 6, 8, 14, 16
144, 148, 152, 154
30, 40, 45, 60
140, 150, 160, 165
10, 30, 60, 80
130, 150, 180, 190

4.6 Teacher Check

Part Five

5.1 3
2
1
3
0
nothing
5
5

5.2 1, 3, 6
100, 30, 6

1, 0, 8
100, 0, 8

0, 3, 7
0, 30, 7

1, 4, 0
100, 40, 0

0, 8, 4
0, 80, 4

5.3 All carried numbers are one.

83	70	61	81	62
133	122	144	121	145

5.4 All carried numbers are one.

13	27	14	18	39
+ 26	+ 65	+ 32	+ 56	+ 41
39	92	46	74	80

3	14	29	53	31
28	3	+ 46	+ 78	52
+ 5	+ 2	75	131	+ 15
36	19			98

5.5 eleven   twelve
thirteen   fourteen
seventeen   eighteen

5.6 twenty-two   fifty-seven
forty-six   eighty-nine
thirty-five   seventy-three

5.7 one hundred fifteen
one hundred twenty-six
one hundred five
one hundred forty-nine

5.8 105   150
102   120
111   116

5.9 Six plus seven equals thirteen.
Eighteen minus five is not equal to
nine.
Forty-six is greater than twenty-one.
Seventy-two is less than ninety.

27 < 51	36, 38
133 > 22	58, 60
53 + 82 ≠ 136	102, 104
47 − 13 = 34	180,182

23	5	86	39
12	11	− 46	− 5
+ 51	+ 22	40	34
86	38		

5.10

$\frac{3}{6}$

$\frac{1}{4}$

$\frac{1}{2}$

$\frac{5}{8}$

$\frac{3}{4}$

$\frac{2}{5}$

5.11

$\frac{7}{8}$

$\frac{5}{7}$

$\frac{1}{3}$

$\frac{3}{6}$

$\frac{4}{5}$

$\frac{1}{2}$

5.12   30, 30

5.13   20   10   10
       30   30   40
       10   50   40
       20   0   10

5.14   20, 40, 20

Part One

1.1   20, 30, 40, 50, 60, 70, 80, 90

1.2   200, 300, 400, 500, 600, 700, 800, 900

1.3   48, 50, 52, 54, 57
157, 159, 162, 165, 166
203, 204, 206, 209, 211
528, 530, 532, 533, 536
880, 883, 884, 886, 888
991, 994, 996, 997, 999

1.4   <   >   >
>   <   <

1.5   four, twenty-four,
three hundred twenty-four

six, sixteen,
seven hundred sixteen

seven
eight hundred seven

1.6   658
791
213
144
964
393
259

1.7   18   256   321   505   762   874

1.8   2, 4, 6
200, 40, 6

3, 0, 9
300, 0, 9

5, 2, 9
500, 20, 9

6, 3
60, 3

5
5

7, 8, 0
700, 80, 0

1.9

4	61	33	5
11	12	2	11
+ 23	+ 4	+ 14	+ 22
38	77	49	38

1.10

fish

fish

The fish and Willy become friends.

Part Two

2.1

2, 3, 5	6, 4, 10	5, 7, 12
2, 3, 5	6, 4, 10	5, 7, 12
3, 2, 5	4, 6, 10	7, 5, 12
5, 2, 3	10, 4, 6	12, 5, 7
5, 3, 2	10, 6, 4	12, 7, 5
3, 8, 11	0, 5, 5	2, 7, 9
3, 8, 11	0, 5, 5	2, 7, 9
8, 3, 11	5, 0, 5	7, 2, 9
11, 3, 8	5, 0, 5	9, 2, 7
11, 8, 3	5, 5, 0	9, 7, 2
8, 9, 17	4, 7, 11	6, 7, 13
8, 9, 17	4, 7, 11	6, 7, 13
9, 8, 17	7, 4, 11	7, 6, 13
17, 8, 9	11, 4, 7	13, 6, 7
17, 9, 8	11, 7, 4	13, 7, 6

2.2

68	88	96	99	88	89
9	12	9	69	78	69

2.3

43	45	61	73	50	73
80	67	54	71	81	53

2.4

786	277	388	878	399	674
395	728	598	849	974	586

2.5

5	5	1	6	9	7	9	3
1	7	0	9	6	1	6	3

2.6	25	44	63	78	14	37
	33	63	60	22	78	37

2.7	233	481	222	713	506	311
	122	433	301	541	623	724

2.8 25¢ 10¢ 5¢ 1¢

2.9 Suggested Answers:

		4		2
	1		3	2
		5	1	2
	2		1	2
		8		4
	3		1	4
		6		3
	2	1		3
		2	1	4
	1			4
		8		1
	2	3		1

2.10

2.11 Suggested Answers:

6:00 P.M.
7:45 P.M.
7:50 P.M.
8:30 P.M.
7:00 A.M.
7:30 A.M.
8:00 A.M.

2.12 2:00 P.M.

2.13	25	36	143	204	315	570

5 + 6 = 11   2   8   14   12
6 + 5 = 11   + 5   + 9   − 8   − 4
11 − 5 = 6   7   17   6   8
11 − 6 = 5

five hundred twenty-seven

20, 25   400, 500   18, 20

6
− 2   4 balls
4

Part Three

3.1 circle - rectangle, square, circle, oval, triangle

line - cylinder, cone, cube, pyramid, rectangular solid

3.2 Teacher Check

3.3	77	55	599	997
	11	11	96	89

3.4 84, 84   93, 93   80, 80

3.5	93	81	37
	25	30	22
	220	841	615
	143	113	610

3.6 third
tenth
seventh
second
first
eighth
fourth
fifth
sixth
ninth

3.7

+		
	6	11
	9	14
	8	13
	7	12

3.8 14, 15, 11, 13, 12, 10

Part Four

4.1 $5\frac{1}{2}$ inches

$2\frac{1}{2}$ inches

$\frac{3}{4}$ inch

$\frac{1}{2}$ inch

$\frac{1}{2}$ inch

$\frac{1}{2}$ inch

$\frac{1}{2}$ inch

2 inches

4.2   yes   yes
                  yes
                  yes

4.3   11
                                 $8\frac{1}{2}$
                       10
       2
       1   1   2

4.4   Suggested Answer:
       inches   feet
       yards   yards
       feet   inches

4.5
                        inches
       My toothbrush is 6 ~~yards~~ long.

                    yards
       The ceiling is 3 ~~feet~~ from the floor.

                 feet
       My dad is 6 ~~inches~~ tall.

                    feet
       The plate fell 3 ~~inches~~ off the table.

4.6   63, 163, 263, 363, 463, 563,
            663, 763, 863, 963

       305, 315, 325, 335, 345, 355,
            365, 375, 385, 395

       750, 751, 752, 753, 754, 755
            756, 757, 758, 759

                        >
                        <

4.10   27 inches
       5 pencils
       42¢
       $4.69
       11 answers
       2 inches
       40 pennies
       20 miles

4.11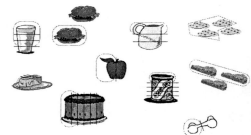

4.12   10
       $\frac{5}{10}$ $\frac{5}{10}$

Part Five

5.1   55   96   379   12   13   89
       54   30   94   62   71   94

5.2   33   15   85   24   11   16
       812   410   612   814   520   111

5.3

Sun.	Mon.	Tues.	Wed.	Thurs.	Fri.	Sat.
			2	3	4	5
	7	8	9	10		12
13	14	15		17	18	
20		22	23		25	26
	28	29	30			

       December
       31
       5
       4
       6, 13, 20, 27
       Monday
       Teacher Check
       Teacher Check

5.4   1:10 o'clock, 9:35 o'clock

5.5 (morning)   A.M.
     (sunset)   P.M.
     (after supper)   P.M.
     (before lunch)   A.M.

5.6 0, 2, 4, 6, 8
     1, 3, 5, 7, 9

5.7 (54) 83 (122) 7 (18) 231 (46) (190)
     7   18   46   54   83   122   190   231

5.8 11   16
     9   14

5.9 75¢, 60¢, 15¢, 3 nickels
     65¢, 63¢, 2¢, 2 pennies
     55¢, 51¢, 4¢, 4 pennies
     25¢, 23¢, 2¢, 2 pennies
     75¢, 72¢, 3¢, 3 pennies
     55¢, 54¢, 1¢, 1 penny

5.10 40   10   90
      40   80   40
      80   70   20
      50   30   20

5.11 70 degrees
      90 people
      100 pages

5.12 2   1
      3   6
      4   5
      6   4
      1   3
      5   2

5.13 sixty-seven
      one hundred fifty
      two hundred three
      eight hundred twenty-nine

5.14 Teacher Check

5.15 14   67   58   68   797

5.16 85   81   575   983   571

5.17 93   71   13   12   12

5.18 722   921   265   301   207

Part One

1.1 thirteen
seventy-six
four hundred nine
five hundred forty-six
eight hundred thirty

1.2 plus
minus
minus
plus

1.3 not equal
equal
not equal
equal

1.4 less than
greater than
greater than
greater than

1.5

66	374
11	502
40	690
71	213
15	942

1.6

=	−	≠
−	+	=
−	=	
≠	+	

1.7

>	<
<	>
<	<
>	<
>	>

1.8 Suggested Answers:

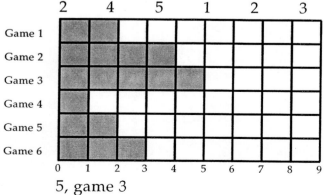

5, game 3

1.9 Suggested Answers:

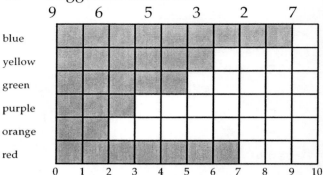

Teacher Check
blue, red, yellow, green,
       purple, orange

1.10

77	98	15	16	99
647	388	42	84	983
9	6	32	71	63
22	11	903	652	322

Teacher Check color.

Part Two

2.1

30, 45, 50	5's
95, 96, 99	1's
130, 160, 180	10's
64, 68, 70,	2's

2.2 Teacher Check
3, 6, 9, 12, 15, 18, 21, 24, 27, 30

2.3

11	6
6	4
12	5
8	10

2.4 12, 3, 36
feet
inches
yards

2.5

88	115	679	545	676
825	996	867	595	987

2.6

33	33	221	362	236
410	123	706	331	611

2.7

7, 8, 15	4, 9, 13	5, 6, 11
7, 8, 15	4, 9, 13	5, 6, 11
8, 7, 15	9, 4, 13	6, 5, 11
15, 7, 8	13, 4, 9	11, 5, 6
15, 8, 7	13, 9, 4	11, 6, 5

2.8
0, 1, 8
0, 10, 8

2, 7, 6
200, 70, 6

6, 0, 7
600, 0, 7

0, 5, 2
0, 50, 2

2, 4, 7
200, 40, 7

9, 9, 1
900, 90, 1

2.9

tens, 90	ones, 9
ones, 9	hundreds, 900
hundreds, 900	tens, 90

2.10
300, 300, 30, 3, 30, 3
6, 60, 600, 600, 6, 60
80, 8, 8, 80, 800, 800

2.11
587, 578, 857, 875, 758, 785
491, 419, 941, 914, 149, 194

2.12 Teacher Check

2.13 Suggested Answers:

5	0	1	4	2	3
+ 0	+ 5	+ 4	+ 1	+ 3	+ 2
5	6	7	8	9	10
− 0	− 1	− 2	− 3	− 4	− 5

2.14
47 — forty-seven
63 — sixty-three
175 — one hundred seventy-five
157 — one hundred fifty-seven
36 — thirty-six
360 — three hundred sixty
475 — four hundred seventy-five
306 — three hundred six
745 — seven hundred forty-five
715 — seven hundred fifteen

2.15

+			
	6	9	3
	12	15	9
	14	17	11

+			
	9	12	7
	8	11	6
	6	9	4

Part Three

3.1
72
27
72, 70 > 20

3.2
584
854
854, 800 > 500

3.3

74, 47	76, 67
83, 38	31, 13
521, 125	932, 239
963, 369	764, 467

3.4

416	460	461	604	614	641
59	95	509	590	950	955

3.5

$\frac{2}{6}$

$\frac{5}{8}$

$\frac{3}{4}$

$\frac{3}{5}$

$\frac{2}{3}$

$\frac{2}{4}$

3.6

14	23	9	98	224
13	76	7	121	28
15	82	10	583	792
100	4	11	114	53
12	3	15	44	81

3.7 212° Teacher Check.

170°

65°
32°

3.8 Suggested Answers:

| 78°F | 120°F | 74°F | 78°F |
| 74°F | 140°F | 68°F | 32°F |

3.9 30°F   68°F   74°F   140°F

3.10 tap water   classroom
hot water   ice water

3.11 Suggested Answers:
ice cubes
cooking

3.12 Teacher Check

3.13 12, 3, 36, 60, 7, 12

3.14 $3\frac{1}{2}$ inches   2 inches

3.15

7	9	200
5	40	8
20	300	10

3.16

| tens | tens | ones |
| ones | tens | ones |

3.17   five hundred seven
57   fifty-seven
four hundred sixty
46   forty-six

3.18 590, 509, 950, 905, (95), (59)

Part Four

4.1 nine dollars and seventy-five cents
three dollars and forty cents
seven dollars and three cents

4.2 Suggested Answers:

4	2	3	1	1
2		3		2
8	2	2		

4.3 $9.73 $6.11 $9.98 $2.24

4.4 $8.49 $1.82 $9.76 $1.10 $5.65 $3.11

4.5
$1.22
+ $2.41
$3.63

$3.75
− $3.63
$ .12

4.6 Suggested Answer:
James paid $2.11 for a hamburger.
He paid $1.32 for the soda.
How much did he pay altogether?

$2.11
+ $1.32
$3.43

He paid $3.43 for the hamburger
and soda.

4.7

11	13	15	10	12	18
4	7	3	6	4	8
9		13		11	
8		2		13	
10		11		12	
9		7		0	
7		4		8	
4		9		5	
6	10	5	9	3	16
4	5	8	9	11	9

4.8 $\frac{2}{4}$

$\frac{3}{5}$

$\frac{5}{6}$

4.9

| 428 | 482 | 248 | 284 | 842 | 824 |
| 248 | 284 | 428 | 482 | 824 | 842 |

4.10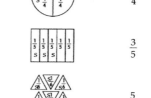

236   six hundred thirty-two
623   three hundred sixty-two
326   six hundred twenty-three
632   two hundred thirty-six
263   three hundred twenty-six
362   two hundred sixty-three

236   263   326   362   623   632

4.11   391, 42, 187
        205, 966, 530, 673
        414, 758, 829

4.12   12:57 P.M.

4.13   eleventh   fifth
        fifteenth   thirteenth
        ninth   seventh
        sixth   twelfth
        eighteenth   twentieth

4.14   eighteenth, ninth, fourteenth

Part Five

5.1   60   30   90
        10   10   40
        100   80   50
        40   10   30

5.2   262, 264   88, 90
        570, 572   353, 355
        699, 701   901, 903

5.3   =   >
        ≠   <
        ≠   >
        =   <

5.4   76   52   91   23   40   62
        37   20   73   81   64   80
        63   82   71   72   70   91
        90   55   94   53   60   54
        670 794 361 671 582
        484 456 343 280 435

5.5   14   24   54   72   62   78
        48   75   60   22   83   63
        21   22   93   16   63   54
        323 704 614 172 284
        824 652 720 315 721

5.6   green, yellow, brown

5.7   Sunday, December 13, –

5.8   10:00 A.M.

5.9   70°F

5.10   12
        3, 1
        $2.64
        1 hour
        yes

5.11   Teacher Check
        8   3   11   5   12   6
        7   2   1   4   10   9

Part One

1.1	5:00	6:30	7:15	9:45

1.2 12, 12
 60, 60

1.3 short
 long

1.4 7, 8
 18

1.5	1:12	8:34	9:08	4:16

1.6

1.7 Teacher Check

1.8

1.9	76	87	78	97	788	769
	13	14	78	129	73	

1.10	14	12	62	45	44	51
	91	63	30	32	14	81
	416	323	115	233	483	
	581	340	255	334	520	

1.11	554	382	824	324	475
	120	642	542	224	640

1.12	41	62	85	38	20	93
	61	73	44	66	55	85

1.13	367	380	754	557	283

1.14 Suggested Answers:
 Bag 1 H toy block 3 ounces y
 Bag 2 (H) dad's shoe 2 pounds
 Teacher Check
 Teacher Check

Part Two

2.1
 17
 256
 310
 509
 301
 526
 13
 44
 265
 999

thirteen
five hundred twenty-six
three hundred one
nine hundred ninety-nine
seventeen
two hundred sixty-five
five hundred nine
three hundred ten
two hundred fifty-six
forty-four

13
17
44
256
265
301
310
509
526
999

2.2
 748
 607
 503
 291
 859
 934

2.3 13
 1, 3
 3, 1
 9

2.4	92	80	74	111	64
2.5	383	894	983	573	672
	570	822	555	971	751

2.6

no
4
13
yes, yes

2.7

no
7
12
yes, yes

2.8	44	37	29	29

2.9   9, 4, 5
900, 40, 5

3, 0, 2
300, 0, 2

2, 7, 0
200, 70, 0

2.10   12 fish
47 glasses

2.11

3, 6, 9	4, 8, 12
3 + 6 = 9	4 + 8 = 12
6 + 3 = 9	8 + 4 = 12
9 − 3 = 6	12 − 4 = 8
9 − 6 = 3	12 − 8 = 4

2.12

		O zero		

1's: 2 3 5 7 9
10's: 14 35 48 76 89 92
100's: 293 349 485 549 722 726 815

Part Three

3.1 568   five hundred sixty-eight
309   three hundred nine
$7.39 seven dollars and
           thirty-nine cents
$4.07 four dollars and seven cents

427	509	756	93
+ 342	+ 154	− 325	− 42
769	663	431	51

6 + 2 = 3 + 5   12 > 5
7 − 4 ≠ 6 + 1   19 < 24

827 872 287 278 782 728

3.2   2 inches
$3\frac{1}{2}$ inches

3.3   yes

3.4   Teacher Check
rectangle, square, triangle

3.5   Teacher Check

3.6   2
1
2
1
6
rectangle, 6
2
2
2
2
8
square, 8
2
2
2
6
triangle, 6

3.7   4, 8, 2
5, 7
bar

3.8

≠	>
=	>
≠	<
=	<
≠	<
≠	>
≠	>

3.9

tens	ones		no
5	14		5
6	4		14
+ 1	9		yes, yes
4	5		

3.10 38   26   29   26

3.11 26   59   29   18
24   59   37   37

3.12 20   10   70
60   50   90
10   10   30

3.13 1 ⊗ 3 ⊗ 5 ⊗ 7
⊗ 9 ⊗ 11 ⊗ 13 ⊗
15 ⊗ 17 ⊗ 19 ⊗

3.14 even

Part Four

4.1 56   92   62   547   797   982
     14   13   79   89   87
     65   33   71   26   43   26
     121 222 705 423 715

4.2 27③   58⑥   1②   1⑨
     ③0   4①8   ②4   8②3
     ⑥58   ⑦02   ⑧61   ②15

4.3 4, 5, 7, 6, 9, 8   5, 7, 6, 3, 4, 9, 10, 8

4.4 4:56   7:07   10:15   2:18

4.5 Teacher Check

4.6
$\frac{3}{4}$

$\frac{5}{7}$

$\frac{2}{3}$

$\frac{5}{6}$

$\frac{4}{5}$

$\frac{2}{4}$

4.7
$\frac{2}{4}$

$\frac{4}{6}$

$\frac{2}{5}$

4.8 $2.30 - 2 dollars, 1 quarter, 1 nickel
     $4.25 - 2 dollars, 8 quarters,
             2 dimes, 1 nickel
       89¢ - 2 quarters, 3 dimes, 1 nickel,
             4 pennies
     $1.37 - 1 dollar, 3 dimes, 1 nickel,
             2 pennies
     $1.55 - 1 dollar, 2 quarters,
             5 pennies
       64¢ - 2 quarters, 1 dime,
             4 pennies

4.9 58¢

4.10 $7.72 $8.76 $4.13 $4.10

4.11

4.12

Part Five

5.1 12, 3, 36
     60, 24
     7, 12
     16, 12
     32
     212

5.2 12
     212°F
     scale
     2 yards
     Monday August 2

5.3   15   7
       9   12
       5   4
       12   11

5.4   60   20
       70   70
       40   25
       35   85

5.5   83   96   871   781   844

5.6   tens ¦ ones   no
       ┌─┐ ┌──┐   6
       │6│ │15│   15
        X¦5   yes, yes
       + 2¦8
       ─────
         4¦7

5.7   8   36   28   14

5.8   14   47   24   68
       39   29   24   18
       46   47   14   44

5.9   Numbers circled:
       3, 6, 9, 12, 15, 18, 21, 24, 27, 30

5.10   3, 6, 9, 12, 15, 18, 21, 24, 27, 30

5.11   3 + 8 = 11   8 + 3 = 11
       11 − 3 = 8   11 − 8 = 3

5.12   6   2   8
       7   6   9   5   3   9
       6   8   4   7   5   9

       Suggested Answer:
          8
        − 2
        ───
          6   Teacher Check

Math 207 Answer Key

Part One

1.1
14, 3, 5, 17
11, 15, 20, 4
6, 9, 13, 12
18, 2, 16, 10
8, 1, 7, 19

1.2
one-third three-elevenths
two-fifths five-eighths
nine-sixteenths seven-twelfths
four-sevenths eight-ninths

1.3
2 years
Monday, Wednesday, Friday
Tuesday, Thursday
$6.44
$2.52
4
yes
$2.12

1.4

11	14	88	99	78
57	128	894	485	859
73	101	90	72	63

1.5

365	984	781	652
892	655	850	672

1.6

23	43	11	52	66
442	382	254	510	

1.7

35	28	18	15
39	14	33	39
28	13	28	6

1.8

$$12$$
$$-\ 8$$
$$\overline{4}$$

800

2

 —pink

Part Two

2.1
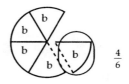

$\frac{3}{5}$

$\frac{4}{6}$

2.2
$\frac{6}{7}$ $\frac{2}{3}$

$\frac{4}{9}$ $\frac{6}{8}$

2.3

$\frac{3}{8}$	$\frac{3}{5}$	$\frac{2}{6}$	$\frac{2}{9}$	$\frac{4}{10}$	$\frac{2}{12}$
$\frac{5}{7}$	$\frac{2}{8}$	$\frac{2}{3}$	$\frac{2}{6}$	$\frac{9}{16}$	$\frac{8}{12}$

2.4
Suggested Answers:
One-sixth plus one-sixth equals two-sixths.
One-tenth plus three-tenths equals four tenths.
Four-ninths minus two-ninths equals two-ninths.
Seven-twelfths minus five-twelfths equals two-twelfths.

2.5
Suggested Answers:
<u>The Little Pony</u>
64, 6
yes, yes

2.6

1, 8	29, 12
9, 10	41, 14
19, 10	55, 10
no, no, 64	

2.7
19
18
30

2.8

October		
10	31	7

May		
5	31	5

April		
4	30	10

January		
1	31	3

September		
9	30	2

August		
8	30	8

December		
12	31	9

November		
11	30	1

June		
6	30	6

February		
2	28	11

March		
3	31	12

July		
7	31	4

2.9
16	12	99	96	68
78	93	896	571	859
54	100	92	83	73

2.10
675	783	472	960	787
581	894	785	620	680

2.11
51	93	20	7	22
512	103	529	300	

2.12
38	24	28	16
28	19	9	4
46	35	46	59

Part Three

3.1
199
299
399
499
599
699
799
899

3.2
128, 129, 130
273, 274, 275
388, 389, 390
424, 425, 426
502, 503, 504
640, 641, 642
789, 790, 791
899, 900, 901

3.3
66	754	537	773	129	133
66	129	133	537	754	773

3.4 penny   nickel   dime   quarter

3.5 0
    20, 30, 40, 50, 60, 70, 80, 90
0, 5
    10, 15, 20, 25, 30, 35, 40, 45
0, 2, 4, 6, 8
    4, 6, 8, 10, 12, 14, 16, 18

3.6
130, 160, 170
590, 600, 620
215, 230, 235
460, 470, 480
606, 608, 614
840, 842, 844

3.7
1②   13②   24⓪   6③
4⑦5   8③   5②9   9⓪4
③61   ⑤94   83   ②57

3.8
7, 8, 5
700, 80, 5

0, 6, 3
0, 60, 3

2, 0, 8
200, 0, 8

3.9
735	753	375	357	573	537
357	375	537	573	735	753

3.10
eleven
twenty-six
three hundred forty-five
two hundred nine

3.11
83	111	104	893	980

3.12
853	928	927	764	727
917	447	809	805	636

3.13
12	3	36
60	24	
7	12	
16	12	
32		
212		

3.14 Suggested Answers:
ounces
hours
degrees
dozen
minutes
pounds
pounds
months

3.15
5	2
10	25
100	4

3.16

3.17
=	≠	≠
≠	=	≠
<	<	>
>	<	>

3.18 rectangle
10
perimeter

Part Four

4.1 no
borrow
6 tens
10
12
yes
yes

4.2
18	16	37	28	55
6	26	16	17	4

4.3
80	80	40
60	30	40

4.4
80	30	70
20	100	50

4.5 50, 60
60, 40

4.6
55¢, 52¢	3¢	3 pennies
85¢, 81¢	4¢	4 pennies
80¢, 71¢	9¢	9 pennies
50¢, 47¢	3¢	3 pennies
25¢, 23¢	2¢	2 pennies

4.7
$ .05   dime
$ .01   quarter
$ .25   penny
$ .10   nickel

4.8
$ .55   sixty-three cents
$ .47   fifty-five cents
$ .63   eight cents
$ .08   forty-seven cents

4.9
$$+ \quad \begin{array}{r} \frac{1}{5} \\ + \frac{2}{5} \\ \hline \frac{3}{5} \end{array}$$

$$- \quad \begin{array}{r} \frac{3}{4} \\ - \frac{1}{4} \\ \hline \frac{2}{4} \end{array}$$

$$+ \quad \begin{array}{r} \frac{5}{8} \\ + \frac{2}{8} \\ \hline \frac{7}{8} \end{array}$$

$$- \quad \begin{array}{r} \frac{5}{6} \\ - \frac{1}{6} \\ \hline \frac{4}{6} \end{array}$$

$$+ \quad \begin{array}{r} \frac{2}{8} \\ + \frac{3}{8} \\ \hline \frac{5}{8} \end{array}$$

$$- \quad \begin{array}{r} \frac{4}{7} \\ - \frac{1}{7} \\ \hline \frac{3}{7} \end{array}$$

4.10 6, 5, 4
     42, 41, 40
     69, 68, 67
     140, 139, 138
     398, 397, 396

4.11

0	1	2	3	4	5
10	9	8	7	6	5

4.12

915	645	808	709
927	979	809	556
918	517	347	649

Part Five

5.1

	70°	72°	74°	76°	78°	80°
Monday						
Tuesday						
Wednesday						
Thursday						
Friday						

5.2 Teacher Check

5.3 603, 630 ,306, 360, 63, 36
     63, 36
     place holder

5.4 fifty-nine
     five hundred eighty-two
     four hundred thirty-five
     fifty
     one hundred sixty
     seven hundred eighty
     one hundred five
     three hundred ten
     six hundred twenty-five

5.5 eleven   thirteen
     twelve   fifteen

5.6

28	125	946	42
+ 46	+ 382	− 531	− 26
74	507	415	16

$$\frac{2}{3}$$

three-fifths

$$\frac{5}{8}$$
$$+ \frac{1}{8}$$
$$\frac{6}{8}$$

$$\frac{3}{4}$$
$$- \frac{1}{4}$$
$$\frac{2}{4}$$

      6
      2   forty-seven
   + 3
   11 crayons   three hundred six
     2, 4, 6, 8   20, 30, 40, 50   41, 40, 39, 38

5.7

2	5	7	10

5.8

57	07	30	39

5.9

afternoon	afternoon	before noon	before noon

5.10

895	164	945	645
51	622	24	26
698	84	585	804
63	300	36	64
622	425	17	33

Part One

1.1   64, 230
27, 947
99, 101 - 757, 759
598, 600 - 545, 547
91, 256
12, 739
46, 622
96, 398

1.2   twos
2, 4, 6, 8, 10, 12, 14, 16, 18, 20
fives
5, 10, 15, 20, 25, 30, 35, 40, 45, 50
ten
yes (or no)
tens
10, 20, 30, 40, 50, 60, 70, 80, 90, 100

1.3

8	10	no

$$\begin{array}{r} \cancel{8}\cancel{0} \\ -\ 5\ 4 \\ \hline 3\ 6 \end{array}$$

8
10
yes, yes

1.4

12	33	19	34	55
28	26	18	55	37

1.5

(72) (93) 84   (67) 46   (30) 56   (84)
−46   −55 −32   −59 −21   −19 −21   −27

(32 − 19 =)   (72 − 37 =)   (94 − 56 =)
47 − 31 =   68 − 45 =   (61 − 42 =)
(78 − 29 =)   (25 − 16 =)   39 − 18 =

1.6   Teacher Check:

72	93	84	67
− 46	− 55	− 32	− 59
26	38	52	8

32	47	78	72
− 19	− 31	− 29	− 37
13	16	49	35

1.7

11	10
9	11
1	8
13	16

1.8

13	(24)	61	(248)	129	457
(6)	(42)	37	151	(286)	593

1.9

<u>3, 5, 8</u>	<u>4, 7, 11</u>	<u>7, 8, 15</u>
3 + 5 = 8	4 + 7 = 11	7 + 8 = 15
5 + 3 = 8	7 + 4 = 11	8 + 7 = 15
8 − 3 = 5	11 − 4 = 7	15 − 7 = 8
8 − 5 = 3	11 − 7 = 4	15 − 8 = 7

Part Two

2.1

+	−	+
−	−	+
+	−	+
=	≠	≠
≠	≠	=
=	=	≠
<	>	>
<	<	<
>	>	<

Suggested Answers:

7	5	5
4	13	15
7	0	7

2.2   753
41
890
502
63
763
41, 63, 502, 753, 763, 890

2.3

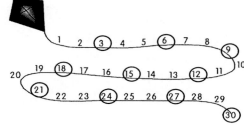

3, 6, 9, 12, 15, 18, 21, 24, 27, 30

2.4 Suggested Answers:

61¢	=		6		1
	=	2		2	1
	=		5	2	1
	=	2	1		1
4					

96¢	=		9	1	1
	=	2	4		6
	=	3		4	1
	=	3	2		1
6					

2.5 $6.84 $8.33 $8.84 $6.72 $7.60

2.6

1			1	4
6	1	2		2
1	2			3
2	1			3
8	2	1	1	
1		1	1	2

2.7

```
  $1.09      $1.53      $8.65
+ $6.47    + $2.28    + $1.17
  $7.56      $3.81      $9.82
```

2.8

59	99	96	111	103
12	14	97	78	69
580	783	915	935	604
288	469	368	569	789

2.9

```
   23       201
  421        22
+  14      + 53
  458       276
```

2.10

20	14	32	23	43
49	18	37	17	64
331	512	312	215	333
57	41	9	77	17

2.11

```
   63        467
 - 28      - 135
   35        332
```

Part Three

3.1 May I play with you?

3.2

=	>
≠	<
≠	<

3.3

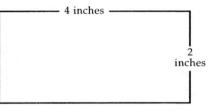

perimeter = 10 inches

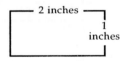

perimeter = 12 inches

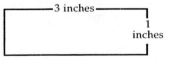

perimeter = 6 inches

perimeter = 8 inches

3.4 2:30 A.M.

9 miles

no

$1.15

yes

yes (suggested)

7 nights

3.5

3.6

2
1
7
1
3

3.7

| $\frac{7}{8}$ | $\frac{7}{9}$ | $\frac{5}{7}$ | $\frac{8}{16}$ | $\frac{10}{11}$ |
| $\frac{1}{9}$ | $\frac{4}{15}$ | $\frac{4}{8}$ | $\frac{2}{6}$ | $\frac{5}{12}$ |

3.8 0, 1, 2, 3, 4, 5, 6, 7, 8, 9, 10, 11

0	1	2	3	4	5
+ 11	+ 10	+ 9	+ 8	+ 7	+ 6
11	11	11	11	11	11

7   0   8   12

6	8	10	12	14	16
15	20	25	30	35	40
30	40	50	60	70	80

```
   85          34          50¢
 - 60        - 18          30¢
   25        16 boys        5¢
                          + 2¢
                           87¢
```

Part Four

4.1

twenty-six   twenty-eight
ten   twelve
seventy-eight   eighty

4.2 six hundred seventy-two
one hundred ninety-nine
nine hundred nine

4.3 three hundred fifty-seven
seven hundred one
five hundred

4.4 231—two hundred thirty-one
312—three hundred twelve
213—two hundred thirteen
321—three hundred twenty-one
123—one hundred twenty-three
132—one hundred thirty-two

4.5

| 50 | 30 | 20 |
| 90 | 10 | 80 |

4.6

30
70
40

4.7 863   620   805   451

4.8

57	138	108	80	46
16	41	104	124	71
85	85	640	832	642

```
   36         327          567         163
   42       + 462        + 225       + 265
 +  5         789          792         428
   83
```

4.9

31	52	22	20	39
111	232	112	522	102
13	29	48	37	26

```
   37          93          54          65
 -  6        - 41        - 27        - 49
   31          52          27          16
```

4.10 triangle (6)
circle (16)
worm (19)
bird (9)
balloon (11)
flowers (2)
hamburger (12)
fish (5)
sandbox (14)
scissors (10)

Graph on next page

orange		✂ 10		blue		🍃 12
🖼 1	18	🐦 9		▭ 14	yellow	
green		🐎 4	black	🎈 11		🍎 3
	🐛 19		GO!	pink	🔴 16	
🐟 5		🐸 5			🐲 20	🌷 7
brown	🌼 2		▲ 6		white	
	red	🐢 17	purple	👼 13		👧 8

Part Five

5.1   9, 4, 2
      2, 4, 9

5.2   653, 356   632, 236
      970, 79   854, 458
      831, 138   620, 26
      443, 344   751, 157

5.3   788   674   507
      380   286   254

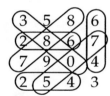

5.4   Some suggested answers:
      cup
      pint
      3
      no
      2
      2
      quart
      2
      no
      2
      2
      gallon
      7
      no
      4
      4

5.5

5.6   12, 3, 36
      16
      60, 24
      7, 12
      2, 2, 4

5.7   60   110   160

5.8   68   68   78   78   97   97
      65   65   91   91   106   106
      14   14   49   49   119   119
     922 922   923 923   602   602

5.9   10   12   31   26
        154   462   626   120
         26   58   16   14

Math 209 Answer Key

Part One

1.1 square   triangle   rectangle
     8 inches   9 inches   14 inches

1.2 5, 2

1.3 10
     10
     6
     6
     yes
     no

1.4 45
     273
     603

1.5 64, 46   53, 35
     873, 378   870, 78

1.6 2, 7, 5
     200, 70, 5

     5, 7, 6
     500, 70, 6

     0, 3, 4
     0, 30, 4

     9, 0, 7
     900, 0, 7

     7, 4, 0
     700, 40, 0

     0, 8, 5
     0, 80, 5

1.7

130	97	173	152	143	114
144	113	181	153	116	69
152	135	137	106	146	115

1.8

68	123	269	774	838
6	17	13	8	
11	12	8	12	
121	96	584	922	741
16	21	89	181	115

$$\begin{array}{r} 87 \\ +\ 36 \\ \hline 123 \end{array} \qquad \begin{array}{r} 468 \\ +\ 230 \\ \hline 698 \end{array} \qquad \begin{array}{r} 42 \\ 33 \\ +\ 57 \\ \hline 132 \end{array}$$

Part Two

2.1 Suggested Answer:
     2
     I like the color.

     5, 4, 5, 3, 2, 4, 5, 3, 5, 3
     3, 5, 4, 1, 1, 5, 4, 5, 1, 5

2.2 3   1   4   4   8

2.3 1   2   3   4   5

2.4

2.5 5
     no

2.6

52	52	144	408	712
3	1	8	5	
8	0	7	7	
8	25	29	48	48
19	27	34	215	518

$$\begin{array}{r} 96 \\ -\ 43 \\ \hline 53 \end{array} \qquad \begin{array}{r} 73 \\ -\ 58 \\ \hline 15 \end{array} \qquad \begin{array}{r} 675 \\ -\ 219 \\ \hline 456 \end{array}$$

2.7 150, 149, 148, 147, 146, 145 ,144,
     143 ,142, 141 ,140

     720, 722, 724, 726, 728, 730

     12 18 15 16
     6   7   12 11

     758, 760 206, 208 380, 382 899, 901

$$\begin{array}{r} 46 \\ +\ 27 \\ \hline 73 \end{array} \quad \begin{array}{r} 58 \\ +\ 29 \\ \hline 87 \end{array} \quad \begin{array}{r} 75 \\ -\ 38 \\ \hline 37 \end{array} \quad \begin{array}{r} 82 \\ -\ 17 \\ \hline 65 \end{array}$$

2.8 Teacher Check

2.9 3
     $2\frac{3}{4}$

2.10   east
south
west
south
east
south
west
north
east
north
west
south

Teacher Check

7 to 8

Part Three

3.1   16
2, 2, 4
12, 3, 36

3.2   less

yes
1 cup

yes
2 inches

108 pounds 8 ounces

3.3   Teacher Check

3.4   Suggested Answers:
7:00 A.M.
7:30 A.M.
9:00 A.M.
12:15 P.M.
3:30 P.M.
6:10 P.M.
8:30 P.M.
9:00 P.M.

3.5   4 inches
3 inches
14 inches
12 square inches

3.6   12 inches   8 square inches
20 inches   24 square inches
8 inches   3 square inches
14 inches   10 square inches

3.7   5, 10, 15, 20, 25, 30, 35, 40, 45, 50

fourth   ninth
third   sixth
first   eighth

3.8   7, 8 6, 9
5, 10
1, 2, 3, 4, 5

3.9   60
30
80
60

3.10   40, 15, 55
70, 10, 3, 83
50, 10, 4, 64
400, 25, 30, 10, 465
25, 15, 2, 42
300, 125, 4, 429

3.11   14   7
18   22
49   79
30   30
90   22

3.12   5¢
7 days
7:08 A.M.
plus 2 minutes
8, 11, 6
linear
10's

Part Four

4.1   65   132
710   560

4.2 eighty-four
one hundred thirty
five hundred six
two hundred ninety-eight

4.3

$$\begin{array}{r} 19 \\ +\,13 \\ \hline 32 \end{array} \qquad \begin{array}{r} 72 \\ -\,49 \\ \hline 23 \end{array}$$

$$\begin{array}{r} 27 \\ -\,16 \\ \hline 11 \end{array} \qquad \begin{array}{r} 410 \\ +\,65 \\ \hline 475 \end{array}$$

4.4
15	16	72	111	102
82	120	591	519	562

4.5   1   2   3   4   5   6

4.6
872	278
320	23
954	459
852	258

4.7
4, 6, 10	5, 8, 13	7, 9, 16
4, 6, 10	5, 8, 13	7, 9, 16
6, 4, 10	8, 5, 13	9, 7, 16
10, 4, 6	13, 5, 8	16, 7, 9
10, 6, 4	13, 8, 5	16, 9, 7

4.8   175, 177   858, 860   399, 401

4.9   70   68   66   64   62   60

4.10
12	26	59	257	645
214	117	527	207	319

4.11

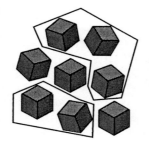

$$\begin{array}{r} \frac{2}{8} \\ +\,\frac{3}{8} \\ \hline \frac{5}{8} \end{array}$$

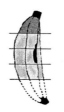

$$\begin{array}{r} \frac{4}{5} \\ -\,\frac{1}{5} \\ \hline \frac{3}{5} \end{array}$$

4.12
$\frac{3}{4}$	$\frac{5}{8}$	$\frac{6}{7}$	$\frac{6}{15}$	$\frac{4}{8}$	$\frac{5}{11}$
$\frac{5}{7}$	$\frac{6}{9}$	$\frac{10}{16}$	$\frac{2}{5}$	$\frac{3}{8}$	$\frac{4}{12}$

4.13
<	>	<
>	>	<
<	<	>
≠	≠	≠
=	=	=
≠	=	=
+	−	+
+	+	−
−	−	+

4.14

+		
	10	12	16
	5	7	11
	3	5	9

5, 4, 11, 3, 6, 9, 2, 8

4.15   three-fourths   one-half
two-eighths   five-sevenths
six-sevenths   one-third
three-fifths   nine-twelfths

4.16 $8.99 $8.96 $3.23 $3.44

4.17
85	85	111	111
639	639	955	955

4.18   52   311   14   29

Part Five

5.1

62   46   65   68

$$\begin{array}{cccccccccc} 7 & 7 & 7 & 7 & 7 & 7 & 7 & 7 & 7 & 7 \\ +0 & +1 & +2 & +3 & +4 & +5 & +6 & +7 & +8 & +9 \\ \hline 7 & 8 & 9 & 10 & 11 & 12 & 13 & 14 & 15 & 16 \end{array}$$

9   17   13   38   14   42

seven hundred thirteen
six hundred thirty-two

36 < 42   64 > 29
16 + 2 = 18   24 − 5 ≠ 20

154

5.2

102	154	383	835	891
14	10	10	14	
11	13	5	8	

834	813	402	933	851
17	14	77	76	108

```
   59        265         36
 + 34      + 425         42
   93        690       + 27
                        105
```

5.7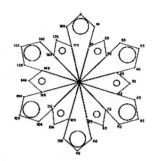

5.3

71	21	224	322	227
7	5	9	4	
3	8	5	3	

36	29	18	24	37
18	25	37	227	312

```
   86         61        872
 - 51       - 39       -327
   35         22        545
```

5.4

22	38
E, E, E	E, E, E
18	10
O, O, E	O, O, E
13	27
E, O, O	O, E, O

5.5   even
      even
      odd

5.6   Suggested answer:

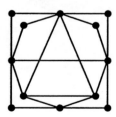

Part One

1.1   997   899   992   675   798
      958   676   678   775   647

six hundred forty-seven

1.2   90   153   111   72   88   92
      893   763   925   595   902
      624   826   575   760   857

1.3   40   20   90
      60   20   90
      80   10   30

1.4   80   90   20
      30   90   40
      60   40   70

1.5   ⑥7   8④2   5④8   5   ⑤3   7⑨2

1.6   300   900   1,000
      400   100   800
      400   300   700
      600   600   400
      300   900   300

1.7   ④3 6   ⑧5 2   7 9   ③0 6   4   ⑤9 7

1.8   A.M.
      180 children
      319 mosquitoes
      Jodie
      20 hamburgers
      360 marshmallows
      $\frac{2}{6}$ pie

Part Two

2.1   4   1   220   41   3
             5   3   8   6
         8   36   16   58   13
       147   124   428   419   207

        45   78   343   961
      − 23   − 29   − 127   − 735
        22   49   216   226

2.2   even   even   odd   odd

2.3   10   12
      O, O, E   Ⓨ   E, E, E   Ⓨ
         17   9
      O, E, O   Ⓨ   E, O, O   Ⓨ

2.4   Suggested Answers:

      2   1   3
           5   8

      2   1   1   2
              6   7
              2   4
                      4   4
              4   1   1
              2   4   6

2.5   penny, nickel, dime, quarter

2.6   twelve dollars and fifty-seven cents
      seven dollars and thirty cents
      six dollars and five cents
      fifty-eight dollars and fourteen cents

2.7 $7.08 $8.22
      $50.62 $15.30
      $42.35 $5.00
      $6.77 $19.00

2.8 $8.17 $7.61 $8.65 $8.35
      $2.13 $3.32 $3.16 $3.49
      $8.29 $9.46 $6.07 $3.11

2.9   2, 3, 6
      200, 30, 6

      0, 3, 9
      0, 30, 9

      1, 0, 7
      100, 0, 7

2.10 326
      503
      160

2.11 thirty-five
      twelve
      six hundred three
      three hundred eighty

2.12 413   17
      582   44

2.13 0, 1, 2, 3, 4, 5, 6, 7, 8, 9

2.14 BIRTHDAY PARTY
Matt is having a birthday party.

Part Three

3.1

| | 70° | 71° | 72° | 73° | 74° | 75° | 76° | 77° | 78° | 79° | 80° |

79°, 71°
June 4, June 5

3.2 10:15   8:02   3:30   1:49

3.3 11:08 P.M.   7:13 A.M.
12:30 A.M.   2:00 P.M.

3.4 60   24
7   12
15

3.5 3
2
10
6

3.6

length: 4 linear inches
width: 1 linear inch

perimeter: 10 linear inches
area: 4 square inches

length: 4 linear inches
width: 2 linear inch

perimeter: 12 linear inches
area: 8 square inches

3.7

108	94	129	120	90
	17		16	
	15		15	
17	12	15	18	16
119	117	111	133	160
619	894	914	603	723

3.8

15	33	33	4	30
	61		53	
	70		83	
150	323	301	411	50
27	16	48	19	47
167	205	214	128	

3.9 <u>3, 9, 12</u>   <u>7, 8, 15</u>   <u>4, 6, 10</u>
3, 9, 12   7, 8, 15   4, 6, 10
9, 3, 12   8, 7, 15   6, 4, 10
12, 3, 9   15, 7, 8   10, 4, 6
12, 9, 3   15, 8, 7   10, 6, 4

3.10

+				
	9	12	5	3
	13	16	9	7
	14	17	10	8
	10	13	6	4

3.11 9, 3, 6, 10, 4, 7, 5, 8

3.12 267   276   627   672   726   762
38   83   308   380   803   830

Part Four

4.1

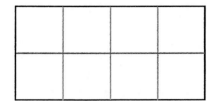

157

4.2

$\frac{1}{4}$	$\frac{2}{6}$	$\frac{4}{7}$	$\frac{3}{8}$
$+\frac{2}{4}$	$+\frac{3}{6}$	$+\frac{2}{7}$	$+\frac{1}{8}$
$\frac{3}{4}$	$\frac{5}{6}$	$\frac{6}{7}$	$\frac{4}{8}$

4.3 $\frac{1}{5}$ $\frac{2}{5}$ $\frac{3}{5}$ $\frac{4}{5}$ $\frac{5}{5}$

4.4 $\frac{1}{6}$ $\frac{2}{6}$ $\frac{3}{6}$ $\frac{4}{6}$ $\frac{5}{6}$ $\frac{6}{6}$

4.5 $\frac{4}{8}$ $\frac{5}{8}$ $\frac{6}{8}$ $\frac{7}{8}$ $\frac{8}{8}$

4.6 $\frac{3}{3}$ $\frac{7}{9}$ $\frac{5}{8}$ $\frac{6}{15}$

4.7   Two-thirds plus one-third is equal to three-thirds.

4.8

69	117	598	999	837
78	97	109	598	478
142	115	96	143	115
573	960		861	913

4.9

42	12	47	42	40
411	453		213	119
36	35	29	24	48
214	525		236	468

4.10   5 months
no
4 hours
yes
3 eggs
perimeter
16 feet
57¢
no
P.M.
35 pounds
4 quarts
no
3 quarts
$7.65
$ .26 or 26¢
3:15 P.M., 3:20 P.M., 3:25 P.M., 3:30 P.M., 3:35 P.M.
2
Tuesday, Friday

Part Five

5.1   8, 10, 12, 14, 16, 18, 20
20, 25, 30, 35, 40, 45, 50
40, 50, 60, 70, 80, 90, 100
12, 15, 18, 21, 24, 27, 30

⟵ west

725, 752

$\frac{4}{7}, \frac{5}{7}, \frac{6}{7}, \frac{7}{7}$

$2.18, $2.19, $2.20

g	o
	y

5.2

14, 16	62, 64	291, 293
130, 132	242, 244	488, 490
855, 857	598, 600	721, 723

5.3

<	<	>
<	<	<
>	<	<
<	>	>
=	≠	=
≠	≠	=
=	≠	=
≠	=	=

5.4   4   3   1   5   2

5.5

2	4	5	1	4	5
3	1	2	4	3	5
3	2	1	5	2	3
2	5	4	3	1	5

5.6   206
369
817
438
762

5.7   five hundred nine
eight hundred thirteen
seven hundred fifty-six
one thousand

5.8 623   two hundred thirty-six
      326   three hundred sixty-two
      263   six hundred twenty-three
      236   three hundred twenty-six
      632   six hundred thirty-two
      362   two hundred sixty-three

5.9 8
     11
     13
     9
     15
     6

5.10 Suggested Answers:

Kari had two quarters and
two dimes.
She had 70¢.
She bought a cone for 69¢.
She received 1 penny in change.

Kevin baked 18 cookies.
He ate 5 cookies.
Kevin has 13 cookies left.

Kari has 3 black cats.
Kevin has 3 tan cats.
Together they have 6 cats.

$\frac{3}{6}$ of the set of tops are
      on the table.
$\frac{3}{6}$ of the set of top are
      on the floor.
There are $\frac{6}{6}$ of a set of
      tops altogether.

Self Test 1

1.01
sixteen — 16
forty-two — 42
eighty — 80
thirty-one — 31
seventy-five — 75
eighty-one — 81
eleven — 11
sixty — 60

1.02
seventeen
twenty-four
eight
thirty-seven
sixty-five
nineteen
fifty-three
twenty

1.03

9	11	17	7	7	10
10	15	7	10	11	7
9	7	8	14	12	6

Self Test 2

2.01

1	7	5	8	3	8
1	5	5	0	4	1
8	3	5	4	5	6

2.02 ②3   ④8   ①1   ⑨6
      1⑤   3⑦   8⑤   5⓪

2.03 28   67   54   32

2.04 ①2   ③9   ⑤7   ⑧2

(twenty) three   (forty) eight

Self Test 3

3.01
12   thirty-three
45   100
seventy-four   60

3.02
=   +
−   ≠
≠   −

3.03
>   <
<   >

3.04
$13 - 5 = 8$
$47 > 43$
$4 + 8 \neq 11$
$65 < 75$

Self Test 4

4.01
<u>4, 5, 9</u>
4, 5, 9
5, 4, 9
9, 4, 5
9, 5, 4

4.02 12   11   98   69

4.03 Mary has ② apples.
Jack has ④ apples.
How many apples do
Mary and Jack have altogether?

$$\begin{array}{r} 2 \\ +\ 4 \\ \hline 6 \end{array}$$ 6 apples

4.04 6 > 5
40

Self Test 5

5.01
thirteen — 13
thirty — 30
thirty-three — 33
twenty-three — 23

5.02
circle — ○
triangle — △
rectangle — ▭
square — ☐

5.03

9	5
15	5
7	6
10	1

5.04 58, 60, 61, 63, 65, 66

5.05 ≠   −   >

Math 202 Self Test Key

Self Test 1

1.01 157, 160, 161, 163, 165, 166

1.02 one hundred twelve — 165
one hundred fifty-six — 120
one hundred sixty-five — 156
one hundred twenty — 112

(lines crossed: one hundred twelve → 112, one hundred fifty-six → 156, one hundred sixty-five → 165, one hundred twenty → 120)

1.03
9	9
11	3
10	12
11	6
8	12

1.04
even	even	odd
even	odd	even

1.05 0
0, 5
0, 2, 4, 6, 8

Self Test 2

2.01
1	4
3	2
4	8
5	6
9	4

2.02
2, 3, 5	7, 8, 15
2, 3, 5	7, 8, 15
3, 2, 5	8, 7, 15
5, 2, 3	15, 7, 8
5, 3, 2	15, 8, 7

2.03 12
60
hour
minutes

2.04 1:00   9:05   10:15

Self Test 3

3.01 155, 157, 158, 159, 160, 162

3.02 3⑦   14②   8⑤   ⑥3   ⑦9   15⑥

3.03
5	4	13
3	33	11
+ 10	+ 21	+ 12
18	58	36

3.04 61   25   12

3.05 second   fourth

3.06 twelve

Self Test 4

4.01 ≠   <

4.02 99, 100, 101, 102, 103, 104

4.03 8
3
$\frac{3}{8}$
5
3
$\frac{3}{5}$

4.04 Suggested Answer:
9, 1, 1

4.05 77¢   76¢   55¢   27¢

Self Test 5

5.01
```
   8
 + 4      12 pennies
  12

  12
 - 5      7 crayons
   7
```

5.02 1 2 3 4 ⑤ 6 7 8 9 ⑩
11 12 13 14 ⑮ 16 17 18 19 ⑳

5.03 even   even   even   odd

5.04 79   88   54   82

Self Test 1

1.01   6   11
          17   12

1.02   1, 3, 2
          100, 30, 2

          1, 0, 7
          100, 0, 7

          0, 4, 7
          0, 40, 7

1.03
$$\begin{array}{r}5\\ +\,4\\ \hline 9\end{array}\qquad \begin{array}{r}14\\ -\,6\\ \hline 8\end{array}\qquad \begin{array}{l}12 > 11\\[4pt]15 \neq 51\end{array}$$

1.04   fifty-nine
          one hundred twenty-three

Self Test 2

2.01   51   71   42   74   51   90

2.02   Teacher Check
          5
          inches
          They always are the same

2.03   43   22   36   23   8   20

2.04   103
          150

Self Test 3

3.01   100, 20, 10

3.02   3, 5, 1, 3

3.03   47¢   22¢ $5.87 $4.47

3.04   34¢

3.05   closed

3.06   no
          triangle

Self Test 4

4.01   12
          12
          24
          A.M.
          P.M.

4.02   P.M.   A.M.

4.03   8, 10, 18
          55, 60, 75
          120, 140, 170

4.04

				16
				8
10	15	15	9	14
				3
				8
6	8	7	0	7

Self Test 5

5.01   1, 6, 3
          100, 60, 3

5.02   98   64

5.03   40   30
          10   10

5.04   thirteen
          one hundred five
          one hundred sixty-seven

5.05   3, 9, 6, 2
          6   35

5.06

Self Test 1

1.01   98, 101   538, 541
        266, 268   810, 813

1.02   four hundred twenty-six
       seven hundred three

1.03   6, 3, 4
       600, 30, 4

       3, 5, 0
       300, 50, 0

1.04

3	52	31	63
20	3	5	22
+ 4	+ 12	+ 40	+ 4
27	67	76	89

Self Test 2

2.01   <u>5, 8, 13</u>
       5, 8, 13
       8, 5, 13
       13, 5, 8
       13, 8, 5

2.02   Suggested Answers:

	4	1	1
1	2		1

2.03

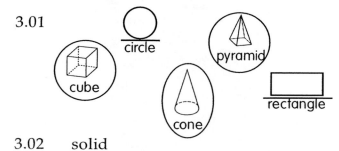

2.04   48   306   250
       seven hundred thirty-four

2.05   75   12   99   569   53   92

2.06   9   5   33   60   234   417

Self Test 3

3.01

cube   circle   pyramid   cone   rectangle

3.02   solid

3.03   84   678   12   99   63   63

3.04   35   31   724   410

Self Test 4

4.01   12, 36
       3

4.02   inches, feet or yards

4.03   24 142 291 369 568 769 812 976

4.04   0, 5

4.05

4.06   98¢

Self Test 5

5.01   12   394   66   112

5.02   50
       90
       30
       80

5.03   Teacher Check

5.04   nine hundred eleven
       four hundred fifty-nine

5.05   75¢, 72¢   3¢   3 pennies

5.06   31
       5
       Teacher Check

Self Test 1

1.01	seven hundred fourteen
1.02	minus
1.03	less than
1.04	603
1.05	≠ −
1.06	10 > 9 8 > 7
1.07	5
	data
	bar

Self Test 2

2.01	4, 8, 10, 14	2's
	157, 159, 160, 161	1's
2.02	12, 3, 36	
2.03	Suggested Answer:	
	sock	

2.04   Suggested Answers:

     3   8   2
     4   1   5

2.05   1   2   ③   4   5   ⑥
       7   8   ⑨   10   11   ⑫

2.06   tens'

2.07   259, 295, 529, 592, 925, 952

2.08   6, 3, 4
       600, 30, 4

Self Test 3

3.01	83, 38	962, 269
3.02	20, 8, 900	
3.03	place holder	
3.04	32	212
	12	60

3.05   (glass with s, s, s) $\frac{3}{4}$

3.06   6   389   99   162   883

Self Test 4

4.01   Suggested Answers:

     3   4   1   2
     6   1   3

4.02 $6.75 $8.59 $4.23 $6.62

4.03   (bar shaded) $\frac{5}{6}$  $\frac{3}{5}$

4.04   Suggested Answers:
       584, 548, 854
       854, 584, 548

4.05   70

4.06   eighth   seventeenth

Self Test 5

5.01   50   90   20   50

5.02   657, 659   299, 301

5.03   13   63   253   13   44   730
       31   85   292   63   62   775

5.04   12   1
       7   1

Teacher Check

165

Self Test 1

1.01   8:19   6:02

1.02

1.03   26   99   688   11   98
        81   511   653   85   292

1.04   16

1.05   ounces   pounds
        ounces   pounds

Self Test 2

2.01   49   sixty-three
        36   four hundred nine
        63   forty-nine
      409   thirty-six

2.02   36   59   5   13

2.03   7, 0, 6

        700, 0, 6

        seven hundred six

2.04   9   65   78   165   191   538   847

Self Test 3

3.01   2
        1
        2
        1
        6

3.02   59   37   34   57

3.03   1   ⊗   3   ⊗   5   ⊗   7   ⊗   9   ⊗

3.04   even

3.05   five hundred nine
        18 > 13   12 ≠ 5

$$\begin{array}{r} 6 \\ 32 \\ +\ 101 \\ \hline 139 \end{array}$$

Self Test 4

4.01 $\frac{2}{4}$ of a jar

        $\frac{1}{3}$ of the jar

4.02

   cone

4.03 $3.55
        yes

4.04   9:44   3:03

Self Test 5

5.01   81   94   17   27

5.02   12

5.03   <u>4, 8, 12</u>   <u>5, 9, 14</u>
        4, 8, 12   5, 9, 14
        8, 4, 12   9, 5, 14
       12, 4, 8   14, 5, 9
       12, 8, 4   14, 9, 5

5.04 $2\frac{1}{2}$

        4

        $1\frac{1}{2}$

Self Test 1

1.01　two-thirds　　one-seventh
　　　four-fifths　　two-eighths

1.02　59　　368　　111　　375
　　　31　　10　　　38　　　45

1.03　14 − 8 = 6

1.04　　2
　　　　4
　　　+ 3　　　9 books
　　　―――
　　　　9

Self Test 2

2.01　$\frac{4}{7}$　　$\frac{6}{9}$　　$\frac{4}{8}$　　$\frac{2}{4}$　　$\frac{3}{12}$

2.02　Three-sevenths plus one-seventh
　　　equals four-sevenths.

2.03　34
　　　yes
　　　14

2.04　9　　8　　6　　11　　5　　1
　　　3　　12　　7　　10　　4　　2

2.05　74　　365　　612　　27

Self Test 3

3.01　thirty-eight
　　　four hundred seven

3.02　0, 5
　　　perimeter

3.03　6, 2, 7
　　　600, 20, 7

3.04　857　　933　　709　　835

3.05　12　　3　　16
　　　60　　24　　7

Self Test 4

4.01　659　　957

4.02　37　　37

4.03　30
　　　50

4.04　803

4.05　362, 361, 360

4.06　　　　　$\frac{3}{4}$
　　　−　　− $\frac{1}{4}$
　　　　　　――
　　　　　　$\frac{2}{4}$

4.07　　75
　　　− 69　　　6 pennies
　　　――――
　　　　6

Self Test 5

5.01　76

5.02　
　　　afternoon　　before noon　　before noon

5.03　forty-six　　　three hundred seventy
　　　four-fifths　　thirteen

5.04　111　　835　　16　　27

167

Self Test 1

1.01 73 257
410 931

1.02 10
70 is a large number. Counting by 10's would be the fastest and most accurate.

1.03 6
10
2

1.04 <u>6, 9, 15</u>
6, 9, 15
9, 6, 15
15, 6, 9
15, 9, 6

1.05 13 (24) (16) 9

1.06 16 37 47 12 28

Self Test 2

2.01 870

2.02 + ≠ <
− = >

2.03 1, 1, 2, 0, 2

2.04 $4.92

2.05 566 857
56 421

2.06
$$\begin{array}{r} 403 \\ 52 \\ +\ 3 \\ \hline 458 \end{array} \qquad \begin{array}{r} 65 \\ -36 \\ \hline 29 \end{array}$$

Self Test 3

3.01 third sixth
fifth eighth

3.02 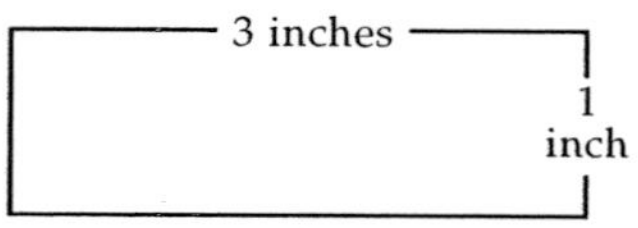
3 inches
1
inch

8 inches

3.03 2

3.04 10 6, 8, 10, 12, 16, 18

$$\begin{array}{r} \frac{2}{8} \\ +\ \frac{1}{8} \\ \hline \frac{3}{8} \end{array} \qquad \begin{array}{r} \frac{5}{9} \\ -\ \frac{2}{9} \\ \hline \frac{3}{9} \end{array} \qquad \begin{array}{r} 50 \\ 30 \\ +\ 2 \\ \hline 82 \end{array} \qquad \begin{array}{r} 28 \\ -12 \\ \hline 16 \end{array}$$

Self Test 4

4.01 one hundred forty
six hundred ninety-nine

4.02 60
50

4.03 103 625

4.04 15 38

4.05 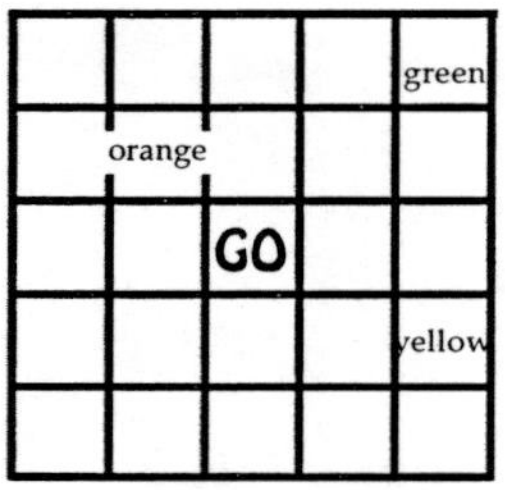
green
orange
GO
yellow

Self Test 5

5.01 865 568
830 38

5.02 2 2 4

5.03 gallon

5.04 12 92 611

5.05 34 47 215

Self Test 1

1.01   3 inches   perimeter = 8 in.
      1 inch   area = 3 sq. in.

1.02   3, 6, 5
      300, 60, 5

1.03   7⑧3   4⑥9

1.04   61   360   61
                      46
             156   + 37
      840   814   144

Self Test 2

2.01   east   north   west   south

2.02

2.03   145   160   15   14   10   2
      49   75   92   61
    + 46   + 38   − 57   − 43
      95   113   35   18

2.04   Teacher Check

Self Test 3

3.01   2   12   16

3.02   P.M.

3.03   10 linear inches
      6 square inches

3.04   square inches

3.05   third
      70

3.06   25, 20, 3, 48

3.07   17
      10
      57
      76

Self Test 4

4.01   73   508

4.02   three hundred eighty
      nine hundred twelve

4.03   872   278

4.04   three-fourths

4.05   <   ≠   −
      <   ≠   +

4.06   82   28 $\frac{5}{7}$ $\frac{3}{9}$

Self Test 5

5.01   28
                      15
                  + 63
    121   82   555   931   106

5.02   53
                  − 28
    24   36   29   236   25

5.03   20
      O, O, E

5.04   15   10
      49   eleven   27 < 45

Self Test 1

1.01 85   113   97   154   50
      778   902   843   986   997

1.02 three hundred forty-five

1.03 600   300   800

1.04 474 letters

Self Test 2

2.01 2   2   3
               7   3
      1   4   1   3

2.02 even   odd

2.03 $17.80 $11.15 $2.30 $5.39

2.04 eight dollars and five cents
      four dollars and thirty-six cents

2.05 $5.50
      $7.08

2.06 3, 0, 8
      300, 0, 8

2.07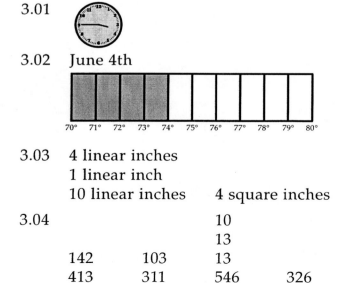

Self Test 3

3.01

3.02 June 4th

70° 71° 72° 73° 74° 75° 76° 77° 78° 79° 80°

3.03 4 linear inches
      1 linear inch
      10 linear inches   4 square inches

3.04   10
                            13
      142   103   13
      413   311   546   326

Self Test 4

4.01 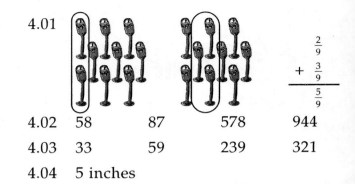 $+ \frac{2}{9}$ $\frac{3}{9}$
                                        $\frac{5}{9}$

4.02 58   87   578   944

4.03 33   59   239   321

4.04 5 inches

Self Test 5

5.01 There were four eggs altogether.
      One egg has hatched.
      Now there are three eggs.

5.02 sphere, cylinder, rectangular solid

5.03 −, =   +, −, =
      −, =   −, −, =

5.04 two hundred thirteen
      eight hundred nine

5.05 $\frac{3}{5}, \frac{4}{5}$ 9, 12 $4.15, $4.16

LIFEPAC TEST 201

1. fifty-seven — 57
   fifteen — 15
   seventy-five — 75
   seventy-seven — 77
   fifty-five — 55

2. twelve
   eight
   thirty-nine
   fifty
   sixty-two

3. 7 9 12 13 11 9 5 6 8 5

4. ⑦4 ⑧6 ⑨2

5. 6

6. 27   98   9   93   22   44

7. 17   40
   sixty-nine   thirteen

8. 4, 8, 12
   4, 8, 12
   8, 4, 12
   12, 4, 8
   12, 8, 4

9. $-$
   $-$
   $\neq$
   $<$

10.   3
    $+\ 5$ 8 nickels
      8

11. $14 - 6 = 8$
    $13 < 23$
    $9 + 7 \neq 14$
    $85 > 62$

12. □ — triangle
       — square
    ○ — circle
       — rectangle

LIFEPAC TEST 202

1. 148, 150, 153, 155, 156

2. 7   16   7
   16   6   7

3. even   odd   odd   even

4. 0
   0, 5
   0, 2, 4, 6, 8

5. 12, 60
   hour, minutes

6. 4:40

7. 32   34

8.   4   22
        3   5
     $+\ 10$ $+\ 31$
       17   58

9.   7
     $-\ 4$ 3cookies
       3

10. Suggested Answers:
    6, 1, 4

11. 6
    4
    $\frac{4}{6}$
    7
    4
    $\frac{4}{7}$

LIFEPAC TEST 203

1. 11   12

2. 1, 5, 7
   100, 50, 7

3. 81   72   91   102

4. 3
   inches

5. 4   4   1   2

6. 85¢   43¢ $6.91 $1.21

7. A.M., P.M.

8. no
   rectangle
   closed

9. 12, 18, 20
   50, 55, 70
   130, 140, 160

10. 50   10   20

11. 134
    102

12. one hundred thirty
    one hundred three

13.

14. <   ≠   +

LIFEPAC TEST 204

1. 532, 533
   300, 301

2. five hundred twenty-four

3. 8, 0, 5
   800, 0, 5

4. 2   1   4
         5   1   4

5. 669   85   63   63

6. 53   521   422

7. 12   3
   36

8. inches

9.

10.   85
    85   − 81
             4

    4 pennies

11. 60   30   50   90

12. 132, 232, 332, 432, 532,
        632, 732, 832, 932

13.   5
      − 2   3 miles
         3

14. Teacher Check

LIFEPAC TEST 205

1. 11 > 10   5 < 8
2. 3
   data
   bar
3. 15, 25, 30   plus 5
4. Suggested Answer:
   box of crayons
5. 1 2 ③ 4 5 ⑥ 7 8 ⑨ 10 11 ⑫
6. hundreds'
   500
7. 732   237
8. place holder
9. $\frac{2}{3}$ $\frac{3}{5}$ $\frac{7}{8}$ $\frac{7}{9}$
10. seventh   nineteenth
11. 12
12.

13. Suggested Answer:

5	2	3	1	2

14.

$7.45	$7.77	$7.28	$3.22	$2.62
49	79	90	24	27
68	76	275	237	311
32	53	597	882	771

LIFEPAC TEST 206

1. 4:56   6:02
2.
3. 16, 12
   pounds
4.

16	18	58	8
58	23	35	24

5. 7, 0, 3
   700, 0, 3
   seven hundred three
6. 2
   2
   2
   6
7. 1 ② 3 ④ 5 ⑥ 7 ⑧ 9 ⑩
8. $\frac{5}{8}$ $\frac{5}{7}$ $\frac{9}{10}$ $\frac{4}{9}$ $\frac{1}{5}$ $\frac{4}{12}$
9. $2.30
   yes
10. $2\frac{1}{2}$
11. <u>3, 7, 10</u>
    $3 + 7 = 10$
    $7 + 3 = 10$
    $10 - 3 = 7$
    $10 - 7 = 3$
12. 671   844
13. 601, 613, 741, 753, 795, 852, 857, 860
14. circle

LIFEPAC TEST 207

1. five-ninths   three-fourths

2. 114   799   664   725
   61   351   26   68

3. 4 + 4 = 8   add one more
   26   minus 2

4. $\frac{3}{4}$ $\frac{6}{8}$ $\frac{2}{9}$ $\frac{4}{12}$
   Two-fourths plus one-fourth
       equals three-fourths.

5. 18 boxes
   $\frac{4}{8}$ box
   2 pennies

6. 11   8   3   12   7   1
   6   9   5   10   4   2

7. five hundred seventy

8. 5, 0, 8
   500, 0, 8

9. 0
   0, 5
   perimeter
   50
   pages

10. 12, 3, 16
    60, 7

11. 72°

12.

   morning   afternoon   afternoon

LIFEPAC TEST 208

1. 18   27
   407   100

2. 7
   7
   5
   15

3. <u>6, 9, 15</u>
   6 + 9 = 15
   9 + 6 = 15
   15 − 6 = 9
   15 − 9 = 6

4. +   ≠   <
   +   ≠   >

5. 1   3   0   1   4

6. fourth
   eighth

7.
```
 ┌── 3 inches ──┐
 │              │ 2
 │          inches
 └──────────────┘
```
10 inches

8.   3

9. $\frac{5}{7}$ $\frac{7}{12}$ $\frac{6}{8}$ $\frac{1}{5}$

10. 80
    90

11. 953   359

12.
```
           north
             ↑
 west ←──────┼──────→ east
             ↓
           south
```

13. 2   2   4
    cup

14. $5.73 $9.95   651   715

15. 82

16. 46   116

LIFEPAC TEST 209

1. 2 inches
   1 inch
   6 inches
   2 square inches

2. 5, 7, 2
   500, 70, 2

3. 8⓪5   ⑨2

4. west   north   south   east

5.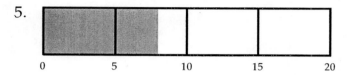

   0   5   10   15   20

6. Teacher Check

7.  P.M.

8.   50
     15
   + 2
   ___
     67

9. 11
   8
   44
   65

10. fourth
    80

11. 85   609
    $\frac{3}{5}$ $\frac{7}{8}$

12. seven hundred eighty
    eight hundred seventeen
    three-fourths   five-ninths

13. <   ≠   +
    >   =   +

14. 20
    odd   odd   even

15. 133   35   328   661 $\frac{7}{8}$ $\frac{8}{12}$

LIFEPAC TEST 210

1. 500   900   300

2. 238 children
   1 quart

3. 2   3   2
            8   2
   1   5   1   2

4. odd   even

5. thirteen
   eight hundred forty-five
   six dollars and fourteen cents
   seven dollars and six cents

6. 30   426
   $7.59
   $3.70

7. 8, 0, 4
   800, 0, 4

8.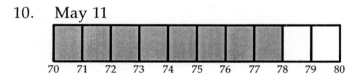

9.

10. May 11

    70 71 72 73 74 75 76 77 78 79 80

11. 3 inches
    1 inch
    8 inches
    3 square inches

12.

    $\begin{aligned}&\frac{2}{6}\\ +\;&\frac{3}{6}\\ \hline &\frac{5}{6}\end{aligned}$

13. −, =   +, =

14. $3.50 $\frac{4}{8}$

15. 130   843   17   516 $9.64 $5.15

175

**ALTERNATE
LIFEPAC TEST 201**

1. thirty-six   13
   sixty-three   33
   sixty-six   63
   thirteen   66
   thirty-three   36

2. eleven
   seven
   fifty-six
   thirty
   eighty-two

3. 10   12   9   11   7   7   7   5   8   3

4. ㊻   ⑬   ㊶

5. 2

6. 39   64   9   78   33   31

7. 13   70
   seventy-nine   fourteen

8. <u>4, 7, 11</u>
   $4 + 7 = 11$
   $7 + 4 = 11$
   $11 - 4 = 7$
   $11 - 7 = 4$

9. $+$
   $-$
   $\neq$
   $>$

10.   5
   <u>+ 4</u>   9 dimes
     9

11. $13 - 4 = 9$
   $47 > 37$
   $16 < 17$
   $5 + 0 \neq 6$

12. circle
   rectangle
   square
   triangle

**ALTERNATE
LIFEPAC TEST 202**

1. 188, 190, 193, 195, 196

2. 11   14   5
   11   8   8

3. odd   even   odd   even

4. 0
   0, 5
   0, 2, 4, 6, 8

5. 12, 60
   hours, minutes

6. 6:50

7. 53   22

8.   5   31
    4   26
   <u>+ 10</u>   <u>+ 2</u>
   19   59

9.   9
   <u>− 3</u>   6 cookies
    6

10. Suggested Answers:
   4, 0, 2

11. 8
   6
   $\frac{6}{8}$
   5
   3
   $\frac{3}{5}$

ALTERNATE LIFEPAC TEST 203

1. 8   9
2. 1, 6, 2
   100, 60, 2
3. 90   82   72   61
4. 4
   inches
5. 6   2   1   4
6. 58¢   22¢ $7.58 $5.41
7. P.M., A.M.
8. no
   triangle
   closed
9. 8, 14, 16
   30, 35, 50
   120, 130, 150
10. 30   40   10
11. 111
    156
12. one hundred sixty
    one hundred six
13.   
14. <   =   +

ALTERNATE LIFEPAC TEST 204

1. 628, 629
   900, 901
2. six hundred twenty-eight
3. 9, 0, 3
   900, 0, 3
4. 2   2   3
        7   3
5. 595   97   73   73
6. 53   521   422
7. 36   12
   3
8. yards
9.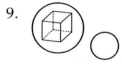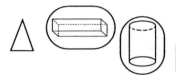
10.   75
    75   − 73
           2

    2 ¢ or 2 pennies
11. 10   70   90   50
12. 147, 247, 347, 447, 547,
    647, 747, 847, 947
13.   8
    − 3   5 blocks
       5
14. Teacher Check

ALTERNATE LIFEPAC TEST 205

1. 12 > 11   7 < 9

2. 6
    data
    bar

3. 6, 10, 12   plus 2

4. Suggested Answer:
    orange

5. 1 2 ③ 4 5 ⑥ 7 8 ⑨ 10 11 ⑫

6. tens
    30

7. 851   158

8. place holder

9. $\frac{5}{7}$ $\frac{5}{6}$ $\frac{7}{8}$ $\frac{2}{3}$

10. third   thirteenth

11. 12

12.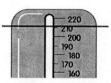

13. Suggested Answer:
    3   2   1   1   4

14.
$4.69	$9.85	$5.56	$4.30	$7.52
37	78	80	33	42
79	69	142	427	512
34	42	588	853	480

ALTERNATE LIFEPAC TEST 206

1. 3:36   7:08

2.

3. 12, 16
    pounds

4. 26   47   56   16
    29   24   36   58

5. 3, 0, 8
    300, 0, 8
    three hundred eight

6. 2
    2
    2
    6

7. 1 ② 3 ④ 5 ⑥ 7 ⑧ 9 ⑩

8. $\frac{4}{5}$ $\frac{7}{12}$ $\frac{7}{9}$ $\frac{4}{8}$ $\frac{2}{7}$ $\frac{1}{3}$

9. $3.35
    yes

10. $3\frac{1}{2}$

11. <u>2, 9, 11</u>
    2 + 9 = 11
    9 + 2 = 11
    11 − 2 = 9
    11 − 9 = 2

12. 495   761

13. 304, 310, 425, 452, 487, 504, 578, 587

14. square

ALTERNATE
LIFEPAC TEST 207

1. three-sevenths   two-thirds

2. 96   697   580   744
    25   322   44   37

3. 3 + 3 = 6   add one more
    50   count by 10's

4. $\frac{6}{8}$ $\frac{7}{9}$ $\frac{5}{15}$ $\frac{2}{12}$

    Four-eighths plus two-eighths
       equals six-eighths.

5. 18 boxes
    $\frac{3}{5}$ box

                    2 pennies

6. 2   4   3   1   7   11
    6   9   5   10   8   12

7. six hundred forty

8. 3, 6, 0
    300, 60, 0

9. 0
    0, 5
    perimeter
    20
    pages

10. 12, 3, 16
    60, 7

11. 78°

12.

    morning   afternoon   afternoon

ALTERNATE
LIFEPAC TEST 208

1. 10   64
    314   500

2. 14
    21
    18
    5

3. 7, 9, 16
    7 + 9 = 16
    9 + 7 = 16
    16 − 7 = 9
    16 − 9 = 7

4. +   ≠   <
    −   ≠   >

5. 2   2   1   3

6. third
    fifth

7.

8. 10 inches
                                        4

9. $\frac{5}{6}$ $\frac{6}{7}$ $\frac{6}{12}$ $\frac{6}{16}$

10. 60
    90

11. 742   247

12.

                        north

            west ←———→ east

                        south

13. 2   2   4
    cup

14. $6.62 $6.72   840   823

15. 82

16. 24   464

180

ALTERNATE LIFEPAC TEST 209

1. 2 inches
   1 inch
   6 inches
   2 square inches

2. 8, 3, 5
   800, 30, 5

3. ⑦3   6⓪9

4. north   east   west   south

5.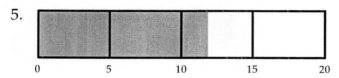

6. Teacher Check

7.   A.M.

8.   25
        20
     + 3
        48

9. 9
   12
   35
   52

10. third
    60

11. 73   514
    $\frac{2}{3}$ $\frac{4}{9}$

12. five hundred forty
    nine hundred six
    two-sixths   four-sevenths

13. <   ≠   +
    <   ≠   −

14. 17
    even   odd   odd

15. 114   28   505   622 $\frac{4}{5}$ $\frac{3}{12}$

ALTERNATE LIFEPAC TEST 210

1. 400   800   700

2. 218 children
   3 quarts

3. 3   1   1   1
          9   1
   2   4   1

4. even   odd

5. twelve
   six hundred twenty-seven
   five dollars and seven cents
   two dollars and forty-three cents

6. 60   283
   $4.21
   $8.50

7. 5, 2, 9
   500, 20, 9

8. (image of apples, 8th circled)

9. (clock showing 1)

10. June 3
    (number line 70–80, shaded 70–72)

11. 3 inches
    1 inch
    8 inches
    3 square inches

12. (two shaded grids)
                        $\frac{1}{5}$
                    $+ \frac{3}{5}$
                    —————
                        $\frac{4}{5}$

13. +, =   −, =

14. $6.40 $\frac{4}{8}$

15. 122   641   37   338 $8.73 $5.14

181